The Ear
and Language

Alfred A. Tomatis

Moulin

Published by Moulin Publishing, P.O. Box 560, Norval, Ontario, Canada L0P 1K0, and Sound Listening and Learning Center, Inc., 2701 E. Camelback Road, Suite 205, Phoenix, AZ 85016, USA.

Requests for reproduction of any portion of this material should be directed in writing to Moulin Publishing.

Canadian Cataloguing in Publication Data
Tomatis, Alfred
   The ear and language

English ed.
Translation of: L'oreille et le langage.
Includes index.
ISBN 0-9697079-8-3

   1. Hearing. 2. Language and languages. I Title

BF251.T65 1996   152.1'5   C96-900143-6

Printed and bound in Canada

Publisher's Note

Moulin Publishing is proud to bring you this first English edition of the classic, *L'oreille et le langage* by Alfred Tomatis. When you read this book keep in mind that it was first published in French in Europe in 1963. The concepts of auditory processing and the role of listening in relation to language acquisition and learning abilities were novel, and to many, revolutionary. Dr. Alfred Tomatis was a pioneer and visionary who demonstrated the relationship between the ear and the voice which is now technically known as the Tomatis Effect. Of his many books this one is considered to be the cornerstone of his Tomatis Method. The original French edition of *The Ear and Language* was part of a scientific series geared to an educated audience. Given the historical nature of this work we have chosen not to alter the style or the phrasing in our translation to allow the English-speaking reader to get as complete a feel as possible for the author and his pioneering thinking.

Other Books by Alfred A. Tomatis

In French

Éducation et dyslexie

La Libération d'Oedipe

Vers l'écoute humaine, (Vols. 1 and 2)

L'Oreille et la vie

La Nuit utérine

L'Oreille et la voix

Les Troubles scolaires

Vertiges

Neuf mois au paradis

Pourquoi Mozart?

Nous sommes tous nés polyglottes

Écouter l'univers

In English

Education and Dyslexia

The Conscious Ear

Table of Contents

Table of Figures

Preface 1996

This English translation of *L'Oreille et le langage*, along with *The Conscious Ear* (published in 1991), promises to further bring the work of my father, Dr. Alfred Tomatis, to the attention of the English-speaking world. In 1994 I was asked to become the President and General Manager of the Tomatis International company in order to increase worldwide knowledge and use of the Tomatis Method. My father's role became that of writer and researcher, while mine became administrator and organization developer.

English has become the international language, and new information about the role of the ear in language development and learning must now appear in English as well as French. In this new preface I present a brief history of the fifty-year evolution of the Tomatis Method, from its beginning in the 1940s to the present time, and provide some comments on its future. I hope that this book, which first appeared in French in 1963, will answer some of the questions I am so often asked about the role of the Tomatis Method in the evolution of sound therapy and auditory integration training.

At the time of writing, about two hundred privately owned centers in twenty different countries throughout the world use the Tomatis Method. They are run by certified Tomatis consultants who come from a variety of backgrounds: education, music, medicine, psychology, physical and occupational therapy, speech and language pathology, audiology, body-mind integration therapy, and others. This book, *The Ear and Language*, clearly establishes the Tomatis Method at the forefront of the emerging field of audio-psycho-phonology (APP), a science invented by my father. APP is based on the premise that the voice can only emit what the ear can hear, so that if you change your ear's ability to listen, you will also change your voice and how you interact with yourself, others, and the rest of the universe.

At the present time, liaisons and partners are being established internationally to expand the Tomatis Method, taking into consideration the culture, business practices, and legal requirements of each country. Tomatis International controls the patents, copyrights, and licenses of the Tomatis Method. The company has evolved through the following six stages, which may hold some historical interest for the reader.

First was the pure research stage (1945 to 1950), which led to the simple discovery that "the voice only contains what the ear hears." This scientifically recognized discovery was discussed in many official publications in its time and remains the basis of our work.

The second stage (1950s through 1960s) was an experimental stage, during which the above discovery was systematically applied using the Electronic Ear. This tool is inseparable from the application of the Tomatis Method and has gone through a number of developmental stages as the advance of technology and research added new insights about the functioning of the ear and the interrelationships of voice, language, learning, and sensory and motor integration. Patents, trademarks, and copyrights began to be used to protect the integrity of what has become a dynamic method of enhancement, correction, and healing for people of all ages.

During the first two stages, the fields of application of the Method broadened to include psychology and education, thus going beyond the original use of improving the musical ear and voice and reducing hearing problems.

In the third stage (early 1970s), we began to understand the uniqueness of the Tomatis Method compared to other methods and to demedicalize its use in the Paris Tomatis Center. A professional training program was established to allow for the expansion of the Method in other countries and the French provinces.

The fourth stage (1975 to 1985) was the stage of pre-expansion, during which the training became more organized, the material became more sophisticated, and new centers were opened in places such as Marseilles, Tours, Geneva, Zurich, Brussels, and Toronto. The centers were created on a small scale, based on a flexible design; after all, the Method was born in a progressive doctor's office as part of a research project that was looking for effective ways to help people when traditional procedures had failed. Communication was easy as long as the number of participants remained small.

The fifth stage, one of rapid expansion, began in 1985. Everything accelerated, and the number of centers multiplied very quickly, with twenty or thirty new ones being added every year. This brought a need to organize training, manufacturing, administration, legal requirements, and communication in different ways. The classic problems of any rapidly expanding company were made more difficult by the non-traditional origin of the new profession, which was entirely unlike anything else in the business world and operated by very different rules. Until recently, the rapid expansion with its attendant economic growth masked the deficiencies of our organization.

Now we are at the sixth stage, confronted by a global recession that began in the early 1990s and continues today. We have chosen not to limit the expansion of the Method to a network of between thirty and forty centers, but instead to believe in the exceptional value of the Method and our obligation to bring it to as many people as we can. My experience in business, marketing, and management indicates to me that we must keep the Method evolving and not depend on stability in this rapidly changing world.

I am encouraged to observe that in the U.S. and elsewhere research is proving the Tomatis Method to be an extraordinary learning tool that improves the ability of a person to distinguish and process incoming information.

Though people in the English-speaking world have only recently learned about the Tomatis Method, they are coming to appreciate how valuable it can be, helping qualified professionals to more quickly accomplish their goals with their clients. I invite you (as part of the English-speaking world) to read beyond the words on these pages, keeping in mind that they were written a third of a century ago. Begin to envisage the possibility of a world where people learn to truly listen to each other on every level. The Tomatis Method can aid in ways we have only begun to measure. I encourage you to contact us if you would like more information about this work.

Christian Tomatis
Paris, 1996

Preface 1963

The mind and spirit of Dr. Tomatis is in perpetual eruption and fusion, like a volcano. He is interested in and passionate about everything. He seems to be in this world to search, imagine, and invent. His volcanic spirit is also a scientific spirit. He will take a barely conceived idea and subject it to relentless experiment until it yields new truths. He can take the most banal observation and derive from it an astonishing variety of scientific and even philosophical conclusions.

For example, everyone knows that noise hurts our ears, and that in consequence the auditory organ progressively deteriorates if repeatedly subjected to excessive noise. After discovering this deterioration among employees of an aviation testing ground, Dr. Tomatis continued, for the space of fifteen years, to study and draw conclusions from this observation. He also discovered that professional singers have a tendency to destroy their own hearing by the sounds they themselves emit, and that this destructive process produces a progressive deterioration of their voices. He concluded that the ensemble of our voice–hearing apparatus behaves like a veritable cybernetics machine. By determining the reactions and counter-reactions of this system, he identified the "Tomatis Effect." Moving from theoretical discovery to practical application, he created the device known as the "Electronic Ear of the Tomatis Effect."

It is clear that Dr. Tomatis is both a thinking man and a man of action. This duality motivates him to move constantly from specific cases to general theory, and then to return to experience in order to confirm the theory; this same method leads you through this book, which contains Dr. Tomatis's reflections, research, discoveries, and hypotheses. It reads like the journal of a pioneer, an adventurer of the mind.

It is not surprising that this book, as Dr. Tomatis describes it, is "an adventure story" and that his discovery dramatically unfolds the connection between our ears, voice, and body. We learn that after the ear had developed into the most vigilant radar for the human species, it became one of the privileged instruments entrusted to provide us with consciousness of the world and of ourselves. We will discover that despite appearances, the ear plays a more important role than the larynx in singing. We will be persuaded that the surrounding environment somehow sculpts our ear and that our right ear does not play the same role as our left. It would be wise to conclude, along with the author, that to speak is to play one's body like an instrument — an instrument by which human thought is expressed.

The journey that Dr. Tomatis proposes to take us on is full of surprises. It is not always easy to follow him; the route may be uncertain, even treacherous, until it develops a viaduct, a way to communicate, and rests on these arches, this communication route, that a spirit had lightly thrown out. Yet it is an exciting road to follow, because unlike conventional, well-traveled roads, and unlike official studies on the anatomy of the ear or audio-physiology, it deals with extraordinary experiences and ingenious observations and directs us toward a psychological and philo-sophical conception of Man. How could we not be grateful to an author who in setting out to speak to us about the ear took us so far along a path of glory, a road whose point of departure is the human phenomenon and whose destination is Life.

Étienne Lalou

Introduction

It is an excellent oil on the head,
which runs down the beard,
even Aaron's beard:
that goes down to the skirts of his garments;
PSALM CXXIII

When you speak, sound pours from your mouth like water over-flowing from a basin. It inundates and spreads over your whole body. Without your conscious awareness, but nonetheless assuredly, syllable waves break and wash over you. Your entire body surface marks their progress through the skin's sensitivity, as if controlled by a keyboard that is receptive to acoustic touch.

Perhaps these first few lines startle the reader. Though the phrase-ology may at first seem puzzling, full evidence of this mechanism will be provided in these pages. The author is confident that his little book will persuade the reader of the truth of his theory: this may all turn out to be an illusion on his part, but it at least had the virtue of sustaining him to the end. The reader need only accept a lovely image for the moment, and imagine a great water-fall, with Self as both source and recipient. The tide produced by the modulation of your own breath flows over your own body.

If you accept this agreeable enough picture and proceed with-out balking, you will be off on an adventure story. What else could you call a book that addresses man and language, presum-ing to explain this knowledge that is always collecting in our human heads without bringing in imagination.

Though progress in our chosen direction is based increasingly on scientific facts established by experiment, we nonetheless still dream of absolutes that will explain the nature of man. Absolutes, however, are not attainable, and we will not search for them.

Instead, using our own logic, and without preconceptions, we will bridge together the chance results that we repeatedly obtained and that are available to any experimenter who wishes to test their truth and precision. As our experience progresses and expands, we will attempt to buttress ever more strongly the bridges erected by our reasoning. Others will come one day and demolish what we build in too much haste, replacing the fragile span of isolated experimentation with the solid structure of empirical continuity, whose logic alone can offer the satisfaction of certainty and completeness.

The reader is invited to join this game of hopscotch and to offer myriad suggestions, which are surely more useful to research than sterile criticism.

This short study provides only a glimpse of the essential nature of language, and of the body that speaks. Each chapter addresses one significant topic in this quick panoramic survey. Readers are invited to delve more deeply into any aspect of these subjects. This book nonetheless contains all the material necessary for the widest possible appreciation of the problem as a whole. Those with an interest in further study will find that there are plenty of books available, written by specialists. The advantage for our reader is that when he pursues one subject more thoroughly, he knows that he is only gaining an understanding of one segment of an unchanged total. He will not let himself be tempted by the cloistered isolation that leads to over-specialized analysis and, in seeking a dizzying drop into the abyss of knowledge, loses touch with reality. Many have drowned at this dangerous sport. Our reader will be able to stay within reach of the surface throughout his adventure, coming up for air whenever he wants and getting his bearings as needed by fitting any new observations into the picture of his overall knowledge.

Anatomical descriptions are avoided intentionally. Since many manuals on the subject exist, our limited space would trap us into a rudimentary listing of the essential anatomical equipment, with the connections between the organs left unexplained. The connections are my only concern; the reader must understand their functional interaction. A few words will fully describe the mechanism involved; there is no need to convey full knowledge of the corresponding anatomical systems.

The first part of the book examines as closely as possible the meaning of the term "language." The definition of language given here is not necessarily the only valid one, but is rather the one best suited to advance the work that has arisen spontaneously out of our clinical research.

The second part deals with our own body, our speaking body.

The body's participation in speech is obvious and total. The whole organism is put into action. This is not simply an intellectual viewpoint; it is a reality confirmed daily by our use of language as the most comfortable means to disclose thoughts, the most elaborate means to interpret them, and the most economical transmitter of symbolic information.

In relation to language, the body can be viewed from two different angles: as a generator of verbal flow intended for others and as a receiver of another's speech. These two functions, essentially different and at first blush seemingly opposite, will be brought together purposefully as we proceed. The only way information can reach others is if such information is primarily personal. Speech makes no sense to others unless it makes sense to oneself. We transmit to others the information we give to ourselves. Furthermore, the information we receive from others can only be appreciated because it corresponds to bodily information produced in others through speech.

To speak and to listen, to emit and to receive are equivalent acts of the same psychosensory and psychomotor significance.

The ear holds the place of honor in our description. As the organ of hearing it is at the same time the gate of entry and the chief monitor of the exit. Both functions will be examined.

In chapters about auditory vocal conditioning, audiophonology, and audio-psycho-phonology, we will see how the act of speech takes form day by day under the guidance of the ear, and ultimately attaining unbelievable skill.

The ear's regulating action leads our attention to the functional dominance of the leading or directing ear. This introduces the problem of laterality, namely right- and left-handedness.

The concept of body image is discussed next. In our study of language, we will see that language is custom-fitted to the body.

The book concludes without deductive pretensions, as its simple aim is to take us back to our original premise, so that we can think through our study from the beginning. The Postscript, added in 1990, provides an update on relevant research.

Language

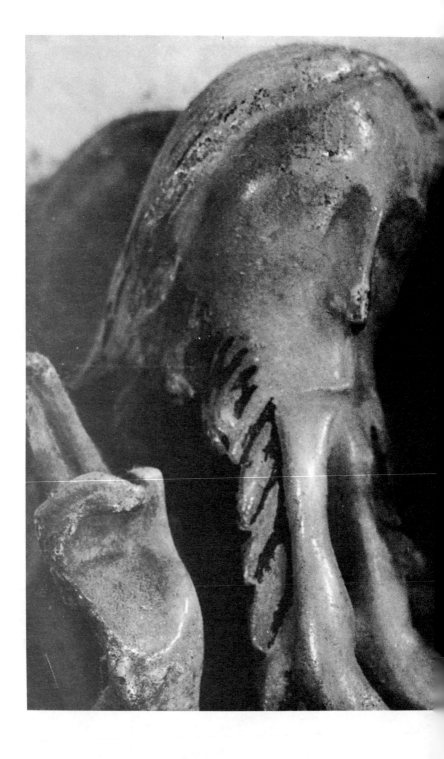

In the beginning was the Word.

JOHN 1.1

■ Language and Man

Man stands in awe of the gift of language. Yet at the same time he feels that language is inherent and that it is a characteristic trait of humanity. He is not so astonished at his marvellous ability that he cannot take it for granted. It does not cross his mind that language could be taken away from him. And although the term *language* includes any and all means of expression, attention in this book is directed toward oral language, the most highly developed and by far most adaptable form.

A man alone, without speech, risks losing his human quality without being able to express his thoughts. Language is his masterpiece. Now the eternal question — which produced the other? Was language born of man, or did language transform the underlying animal into the human? The question seems destined to remain unanswered because, at our level, no real answer exists. For our purposes here, let us assume that an exceptional combination of circumstances endowed us with that good sense to adopt language for our communal use, in family and social life. It came from a desire for communication, and the need to impart one's impressions to others and to receive and remember the knowledge gathered by others. Imagine to what extent man has since affected language and how language has helped to shape man. Word as creator is inconceivable apart from thought.

Word and thought are not disassociated in the Logos. The Word existed before the creation of the world. The divine issue of the Word set in motion the first Thought, object of the supreme Point of Creation. Word-Thought preceded the Word, origin of all light. This Word, immaterial, disembodied, in existence before the world, was nevertheless one day made manifest. It marked the beginning of the world, and by its modulation the world proceeds. All human thought is indivisible from world Thought. Man's cosmic presence makes him a cell inseparable from its environment. His word, his language in short, will be part of the cosmic Word whose creative force guides his will to live and will act as a unit within the milieu that engulfs him.

As the diminished and surely imperfect image of a cosmic whole, man has become aware of the Word-Thought within him. The Word enables him to externalize the pre-existing Word-Thought, giving him the deeply rooted feeling of having created something.

We know the consequences of this line of reasoning, or perhaps we should call it raving!

Man can create with the spoken word a way to increase his human potential. Through it he can observe and know himself. Day by day his mode of expression expands, along with his powers of self-investigation. As he participates in a social structure, its collective tolerances define and impose personal limitations within a somewhat rigid framework. These limitations are true borders to his individual freedom, yet his participation provides him with the possibility of expanding the level of his consciousness to the very limits of human Thought. Language is the vehicle that carries man ever farther and higher in the development of thought. It is his springboard into a dimension where words are no longer useful, where Word-Thought can exist unsupported, beyond the gravitational pull toward matter that is exerted by the spoken word.

The phenomenon of language thus occurs between two poles

of silence. At one end is the muteness of one who knows nothing and cannot say anything, whose main concern is to hide his lack of desire to communicate lest it betray his low humanization level. At the other end is the silent pinnacle of meditation of one whose power and refinement of language take him to the utmost heights of the Word of man.

Depending on his human level of growth attained, man ranges between these two extremes. He uses the instrument of language to reconcile the animal he knows himself to be, which belongs to the material world, with the cosmic thought that constantly affects him and in which he bathes.

Specialists from varied backgrounds turn to the problem of language. Often they reach it after a long journey, during which they retain strong ties to their original training. Their prior knowledge filters the areas they illuminate with whatever clarity and vividness are born in the shadows of their former preoccupations.

■ Language and the Philosopher

Wise men give answers that fail to satisfy our eternal, irrepressible need for unity. We are ceaselessly driven back and forth between the search for a point of origin and our quest for the universal container. Can we be satisfied when the problems under attack deal with human phenomena? If the philosopher ever spoke the whole truth, in this or any other instance, he would cease to be a man, and all these problems would disappear in obvious solutions and no longer have to be considered. We need not worry, for anyone who claims to have reached this point will not be understood, because he will have exceeded man's perspective. As Pythagoras liked to think, "No man is wise, only God."

Like other men, therefore, the philosopher has to solve problems, and his solutions depend wholly upon the parameters he

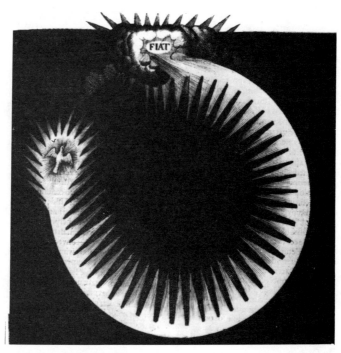

FROM THIS POINT WHICH MARKS THE GENESIS OF MAN FROM THE BEGINNING OF TIME AND SPACE.

selects using his essentially human mental equipment. Choice of factors is all-important. If too many are selected, they scatter and quickly lose their coherence, and the philosopher's field of consciousness has trouble following them. If too few, the consequent polarity grotesquely deforms his judgment of the results. We deliberately avoid mentioning that enormous distortions arise when a problem is badly framed or when the problem-solving strategy is poorly carried out.

Furthermore, the philosopher's only purpose in defining the Logos is to fit human existence into the general frame of his world concept; our unconscious tends to drag us along with him irresistibly, toward the origin of all things. From this point, which marks the genesis of man from the beginning of time and space, we see man as born either of God or of Earth, depending on our deepest personal tendencies. "If man is of divine origin," said

Goethe, "so is language; if man is an earth being, then language is also a natural fact."

In either case the philosopher has plenty of metaphysical proofs upon which to base his theories. His arguments gravitate toward some favorite point, which is peculiar to his fundamental resonance.

Thus we find ourselves pulled in opposite directions. On one side are fanatical defenders of homogenesis, which may or may not be founded on theological concepts. On the other side, promoters of empiricism push to extremes against their opponents' determinism.

The commanders of determinism and empiricism fight for their cause, each beneath his own flag, but without necessarily using the same arguments.

The determinists back the theory of homogenesis and deny all human intervention in the origin and development of language. This extreme position is adopted by W. Wundt who neither sees any human intervention in the origin of language nor admits that, once acquired, language could evolve on its own. W. von Humboldt leans toward the same conception, stating that "language was human from the beginning." The absence of the same anthropological factor also characterizes the opinion of E. Renan on the origin of language, when he tells us that nature has endowed man with speech, which he considers a mere faculty, like that of sign or interpretation. H. Steinthal and Benedetto Croce took the same stand.

To admit that man is as he is provides no solution to the origin of language nor enlightenment about the origin of man himself. The question of what preceded language in man's prehistory remains in total darkness. With no prior step, this speaking animal springs up out of a soup, like a thousand-faceted crystal bloc, securely enriching us when we want to penetrate this initial mystery.

Whether he is of divine origin, the finite creation of a single will, as stated by Plato in *Cratylus* and Aristotle in *On Interpretation*

LANGUAGE AND THE PHILOSOPHER

(viewpoints blindly backed by certain theologians such as Juste Lipse, Vossius, and Dom Calmet) or of earthly extraction (the fruit of a conjectured anomaly, locked in place by an obscure catalysis, as stated by Wundt, von Humbolt, Steinthal, and Max Muller), man as we know him seems to rise out of the dawn of time without prehistory. Spontaneous generation is obviously hard to accept, especially since some of its supporters reject the creative genius of man. It therefore provides an easy target for the violent objections of its adversaries, who have taken full advantage, to the point that they are guilty of an easy and abusive extremism. The empiricist grounds his opposition on man's will and intelligence and bases the construction of the act of speech on experience. Imitation, analogy, invention, and the biological and social need for communication are advanced in turn.

"Every step in the formation of language is conscious," declares A. Marty, thus taking a firm stand directly opposed to Wundt.

Marty later rephrased this statement under pressure of Wundt's violent attack labeling him the champion of the "theory of pure invention." Marty, however, was only zealously counting himself among the line of empiricists who had gone before him: Condillac, Tiederman, Darwin, Spencer, Geiger, Taylor, Carus, Schlegel, Michelet, and Madvig.

So we are poised between two assumptions: on the one hand, that language existed from the start without any contribution by man, and on the other, that man gradually fashioned language through increasingly complex communal and social experimentation. Regardless of whether it is an inherent human faculty or the discovered and evolved tool essential to becoming human, language is difficult if not impossible to separate from thought. We cannot determine at what precise moment language came into being in its own right. Perhaps it sprang up one day, like fire shooting out of the first spark, from between the hands of man.

Why not a Word Age, preceding in time the Iron Age, the Fire Age, or the Stone Age?

According to a definition borrowed from Revesz, "Language is a set of meaningful signs making it possible to distinguish objects of the external world and states of mind by means of a fixed co-ordination between the signs and their meaning." Revesz reveals his wish to abolish the no-man's-land separating determinists from empiricists. Undoubtedly he is right in thinking that both groups fanatically support positions backed by pertinent but insufficient and incomplete arguments. He wants to bridge the gap and show that when the explanations are conjoined, they may throw light on a wider field of investigation. Biological and social elements result in a contractual theory that says language occurs as the consequence of the need to communicate, emanating in turn from the instinct for communal life. In man more than in any other animal, psychism, the condition of being psychic, makes possible the development of this method of relating, which is used by man to externalize and expand his inborn tendency toward symbolism.

■ Language and the Linguist

Others who are closer to the scientific method remove themselves from risk and from taking a chance on unfounded thought and henceforth submit themselves to the rigors of following systematic observation. They thus abandon the cosmological dimension in order to cautiously consider facts that have been gathered, recorded, carefully compiled, and compared. This approach gives birth to linguistics, a discipline that on a macroscopic scale defines the science of language as the study of language as a system. In its very purpose, linguistics makes an essential distinction. The linguist's concern henceforth is not in language as the prime element in exploiting the possibilities of acoustic communication, but rather in the product of this approach. The linguist's resolution is to consider the product as the essential fact. In short, linguistics is the study of distinct tongues rather than of the wider human phenomenon of language.

This science has achieved its individuality through the timid sprouting of seeds planted over the last few centuries, which only reached maturity around the beginning of the 1800s.

How difficult it would be to detect in our characteristically human verbal outflow all that this exterior unconscious act can embody of tightly woven and entangled thought.

The hope of finding a common tongue gave rise, no doubt, to the first investigations on the origin not of language, but of tongues.

Our Western outlook separated us for a long time and led us to believe that everything came from Latin and Greek, and we also had an obscure feeling that there could be no language older than that of the Bible. Hebrew long and religiously enjoyed the exclusiveness granted to the chosen tongues. But despite the impenetrable fortress of its sacred character, Hebrew fell before the assault of the Lebanese Maronites, under the leadership of Théodoret, Amira, and Myricoeus.

Some made foolish attempts to elevate their own particular dialect to the rank of the original human language. Pezron and Pelloutier spoke in defense of Breton; T. de Sorreguieta, D.P. de Astraloa, and J.B. Erro around the beginning of the last century placed Basque at the summit of the linguistic hierarchy; Goropius Becanus, Adrien Van Schrieck, and de Grave claimed that position for Flemish; La Tour d'Auvergne and Court de Gebelin chose Celtic. For anecdotes, we could cite the example reported by Mario Pei in *The Story of Language:* around the beginning of the seventeenth century a Swedish philologist seriously maintained that in the Garden of Eden God spoke Swedish, Adam spoke Danish, and the Serpent spoke French. The same author goes on to tell us that at a Turkish linguistics congress held in 1934 it was

HEBREW LONG AND RELIGIOUSLY ENJOYED THE EXCLUSIVENESS GRANTED TO THE CHOSEN TONGUES.

as seriously argued that Turkish is at the root of all languages.

On the other hand, since the time of Leibnitz, huge language collections were published in order to compile samples of various tongues for comparative purposes. Most important among these documents was the one published by the Spanish Jesuit Hewas in Cesena and the one put out by Catherine II in St. Petersburg on the tongues of Europe, Asia, and Africa.

The propagation of the Christian faith led to the translating of the *Lord's Prayer* into nearly all existing languages. This comparative document proved very useful to linguistic research.

When England took over India near the end of the eighteenth century, the discovery of Sanskrit, transmitted unchanged as a holy language, brought to light a verbal world three thousand years old, the source of the languages that were to spread over Europe. Historical linguistics became the history of people. By examining successive modifications in pre-existing languages, the influence of the sweeping linguistic invasion descending from the flanks of the Tibetan peaks was determined. In most cases the effect was similar to a flood tide. Usually, little or nothing was sometimes left of the aboriginal tongues. Every invasion deposits a new layer over the preceding layer, which is by then already greatly amalgamated with local idioms formed during each interval.

Indo-European, the melting pot of present-day language, sourced from Sanskrit, is no longer considered to be the first language to exist on our globe. The very fact that its advancing waves were said to have drowned out the tongues of men who had gone before leads us to suppose that Sanskrit was preceded by other tongues, which by spoken communication permitted communal life as we imagine it.

The dream of finding in Sanskrit the first tongue could not be maintained in the face of essentially different yet flourishing language groupings such as Hebrew and Chinese. Just like Sanskrit,

Character Zoographus.	Figura literarum vulgaris.	Græcorum ad eas affinitas.
	ⲁ ⲁⲅⲁⲑⲟⲥ ⲇⲁⲙⲱⲛ *dicitur, id eft,* Bonus Dæmon.	Λ
	Γ ⲅⲁⲙⲁ⳽ *dicitur, id eft,* Norma.	Γ
	ⲇ ⲇⲁⲗⲧⲁ *dicitur, id eft,* Bonus ager.	Δ
	Υ Proceffus inferiorum ad fuperiora fymbolum eft.	Υ
	O ⲟ⳾⳾ *dicitur, id eft* Mundi Dominus.	O
	λ ⲗⲁⲃⲇⲁ *dicitur,* Proceffus fuperiorum ad inferiora.	Λ
	X Proceffus animæ mundi ἄνω ⳽ κάτω.	X

IN THE VIEW OF THE LINGUIST, LANGUAGES ARE BORN, DEVELOP AND EVOLVE...

their zone of influence became evident, and their family tree was traced out.

In his study of languages the linguist then took on the guise of a zoologist. In his view languages are born, develop, evolve, expand, and bloom, and at times they shrink, break down, and regress. From 1875 on, Whitney took the lead in this study of the life of languages by establishing the laws that govern their transformations. He described laws of economy and convenience and the composite effect of opportunity in determining the choice of linguistic material in each language. However, Whitney and his followers Sayce, Sweet, and Jespersen appeared too rigid in confining the evolution of language to a system strictly ruled by preestablished laws.

Bréal was more flexible and open to the influence "of an obscure will" and sought the aid of unconscious acts; previously will alone had been looked upon as the determinant of the evolution of language. To justify his position, Bréal sought in the mechanisms of language formation the symbolic, significant part that generates them. This attitude opened the way to semantics, Bréal's last refuge.

As linguistics has progressed, coordinates of its field of activity have become more precise. Linguistics abandoned the dream of discovering the first words, leaving it to Herodotus, who relates in his second book of stories the anecdote about King Psamtik, who decided to wait for the first sounds emitted by two babies who had been isolated from the world, nursed by goats, and deliberately never exposed to the human voice.

The linguist also ranged over his self-appointed domain in the guise of "naturalist," as Schleicher liked to put it. Imbued with the same principles, Abel Hovelacque defined linguistics as "the science that studies the phenomenon of articulated language and its products." He compares linguistics to physiology, which studies the functions of the body. Linguistics traces language evolution (whether normal, modified, or disturbed) following Darwinian principles dear to Schleicher.

The purpose of linguistics, based on observation, experimentation, and evolution, became so prodigiously documented that the science was forced to create such vast departments that it was pushed to its limits.

As a descriptive science, linguistics compiles all that human genius is capable of analyzing.

Linguistics becomes historical when it meets the study of the evolution of tongues, basing its documentation on comparative grammar.

As a generalized science, linguistics views language as a system of signs that derive their meaning from a social medium born of the needs of communal living.

This distinction in the twofold activity of the linguistic sign recalls Ferdinand de Saussure's work. In *Cours de linguistique générale* he stresses its value in terms of the meaning it carries (the signified) as designated by its manifestation (the signifier). As stated by E. Benveniste: "The signifier is the phonic translation of the Concept; the signified is the mental counterpart of the signifier."

In *Linguistique*, Jean Perrot, from whom we borrowed the above quotation, says that de Saussure's concept recognizes the arbitrary element in the choice of the signifier, except for onomatopoeia and the instinctive words termed "of elementary affinity" by H. Schuchardt. In this de Saussure approaches the Encyclopedists who say that "words do not necessarily have any relationship with the meaning they are intended to express." Leibnitz related this opinion in 1703 in *Nouveaux Essais sur l'entendement humain [New Essays Concerning Human Understanding]*: "There is no natural connection between certain articulated sounds and certain ideas, but an arbitrary institution took place by virtue of which a given word was voluntarily the sign of a given idea."

This way of looking at language, characteristic of de Saussure's theory, has borne ample fruit. It provided a measure of sorts for the values to be attributed to the two parameters *signified* and *signifier*. To speak of measure, units had to be found. In *Éléments de linguistique générale*, Martinet introduces with his customary precision what he calls the double articulation of language: "The first articulation of language is the one whereby any fact of experience to be transmitted, any need one wishes to communicate to another, is analyzed into a series of units each possessing a vocal form and a meaning." The second articulation of language concerns itself particularly with the succession of analyzable units within the vocal form, without worrying about whether or not these units have any meaning.

To obtain units involved in the first articulation, reduce the signifier-signified pair defined by de Saussure to a minimum beyond which the pair no longer has the value of a meaningful sign. Martinet proposed the term "moneme" for this unit. The moneme, which is not merely identical to the word, breaks down into "semanteme" (Martinet prefers "lexeme") and "morpheme." The semanteme or lexeme indicates the lexical sense, while the morpheme indicates the grammatical sense or the form. In the second articulation the unit at the limits of auditory analysis has been designated "phoneme."

The physicist pursues his investigation while linguistics is taking on the appearance of a system of systems, as J. Perrot and V. Brondal have put it.

The acceptance of these interlinked systems allows broader and more precise notions of language. Language is a whole; there can be no question of isolating its evolution and studying it word for word as etymologists did for a long time, marveling at how verbal roots emanating from ancient languages jumbled from cascade to cascade down to their current forms. It is likewise impossible to suppose that a language can be viewed as a configuration determined and designed by a static study, in direct contradiction to the state of motion characteristic of interreacting systems. Language can only be viewed as an evolutionary process whose changing parameters can be seen in cross-sections showing the static image of the process at a given moment. Ferdinand de Saussure, who strongly advanced this notion, foreshadowed the distinction between evolutionary linguistics (termed *diachronic* or "through time") and static linguistics (termed *synchronic* or "with time").

From de Saussure's work also came the idea that the fascinating dichotomy of sign into signified and signifier applies equally to the study of either 1) the vocal act within a spoken sequence, whatever the language, or 2) the language itself using elements collected during the study of the vocal act. These two studies are distinct, yet they can only exist together. The former characterizes the science of speech sounds, the latter that of language sounds.

Ferdinand de Saussure's disciples, such as A. Meillet, C. Bally, and A. Sechehaye, have felt the necessity of this distinction even more than the master of the Geneva School himself.

Phonology emerged mainly from the linguistic circle of Prague founded in 1926 through the efforts of N. S. Troubetzkoy, R. Jakobson, and S. Karcevskij. Its sole self-declared concern is the study of language sounds.

The Prague group was greatly inspired by a Pole, J. Baudouin de Courtenay. N. S. Troubetzkoy reported in *Grundzüge der Phonologie* that they developed the notion of the coexistence of a science of concrete sounds (subject to laboratory analysis as physical phenomena and corresponding to phonetics) and a science "of phonic signals used for the purpose of mutual understanding within a linguistic community."

He also reports that phonetics is "the science of the physical production of human language sounds, while phonology does not count on this function of language.

■ Language and the Phonetician

The phonologist is above all a linguist, whereas the phonetician interprets language as if through an auditory microscope. Long accustomed to appreciating the value and quality of sounds, the phonetician is master at deciphering language. He dissects the various constituents of a spoken sequence down to the finest detail without really worrying about their symbolic content. What matters to him "is the analysis of the fragment he is handed; the rest is the business of the linguist or of the semanticist." At first it seems difficult to specialize so much within what purports to be the same subject, that of language; yet music provides a parallel classification with studies ranging from harmony and counterpoint to the simplest solfeggio.

The phonetician is skilled in musical linguistic dictation, and knows how to transcribe any linguistic unit into a unit of sound. The simplest sound is the phoneme. Ideally, the phonetician wants to represent the acoustic content of all languages by a single set of characters, which strictly correspond to pronunciation and adhere to the spoken text. It would no doubt be a marvelous dream to write down what one heard, instead of having to translate it into conventional signs of primitive shape. But this dream is far from being reality and meets with many stumbling blocks. A great many unusual signs must be learned before they can be read, and only a skilled specialist, with a phonetician's ear could perceive them all. Applications of phonetic writing are thus severely limited. Still, the introduction of phonetic writing smoothed difficulties that arose whenever one had to graphically capture what the ear heard.

In short, to be a good phonetician one must have good hearing; without it phonetic writing cannot easily transmit the proprioceptive sensations it aims to reproduce. To be a phonetician it is not enough to be endowed with a phonetically established

ETCHING DRAWING OF A SONOGRAM OF *ALEPH*.

atificial pronunciation. Phoneticians ought to realize that their signs, which rigorously define sounds, are of value only to themselves and to those who have a good ear. They tend to forget that their highly trained sense of hearing gives them a distinct advantage in carrying out their analysis. No judge is worse than the musician who cannot conceive that others may not have and benefit from perceptive abilities like his own.

These new signs are nothing but the translation of acoustic phenomena. If a bad integrator makes the translation impossible, phonetics do not exist. Phonetics lets the uninitiated know that differences exist in sounds, just as conventional signs allow a colorblind person to distinguish differences between colors. Even so, the latter could not presume to use those colors with the same skill as a painter with normal vision. As Daniel Jones declares in *An Outline of English Phonetics:* "No one can presume to be a competent specialist in the field of linguistic phonetics if he is not furnished with an excellent ear."

■ Language and the Physicist

What the phonetician glimpses through his sharp hearing, the physicist can use as evidence in his laboratory. Many instruments can transfer language onto a visual plane and break down into measurable particles all the sound included in any given language. At his disposal is a great variety of sound investigating tools, which unveil in fullest detail the mysterious mixtures contained in the spoken word.

Here more than elsewhere language is perceived as a system of systems. Its physical structure is best revealed by separating its elements into the essential characteristics of any sound: intensity, pitch, timbre, and duration.

"Sound" in a spoken sequence is not a simple element. Quite the contrary. Even though to the phonetician it constitutes a sufficient and necessary unit, its physical structure is highly complex. Before we tackle the physical study of language sounds, it is good to review the effect of sound on the physical plane.

A pure sound is the simplest place to begin our examination. A product of the laboratory and rarely found in nature, a pure sound is one that has a single frequency.

Frequency determines the pitch of a sound. Pure sounds are distinguished from each other by their tonal pitch, that is, by the frequency of vibrations from the emitting source. Low sounds produce a limited number of vibrations in the medium, whereas shrill sounds are generated by a multitude of vibrations. A sound can interchangeably be referred to as having a specific number of cycles per second (cps), periods, or hertz (Hz). These various terms all designate the number of double frequencies per second. Frequencies are double, in effect, because they correspond to a full oscillation in both directions around a position of equilibrium whenever the source produces a vibration in the encompassing medium.

Sound travels 330 meters per second in dry air at 0°C. The distance covered in one second by the initial vibration, which originates at the source, expands continuously. Each of the excited points transmits its energy in turn to the next adjacent point at a specific speed of propagation.

Another measurable parameter of sound is intensity. It has no effect on speed and depends on the amplitude of the initial vibration. It fades with distance, indicating that loss of intensity is a function of the space traveled.

In other words, the quality and characteristics of a pure sound can also be determined by the length of time it lasts.

A graphic representation of a sound shows that a pure sound is characterized by a sine curve along an axis that indicates time.

By successively balancing a point predetermined at the start of the vibration, the frequency can be noted as a function of the number of cycles per second.

What we have described is the simplest case, limited to pure sound. Everything becomes more complicated when dealing with so-called complex sounds, which have a timbre peculiar to the mixture of their components.

Various instruments called analyzers help us study sounds.

■ Language and Us

It would be nice to be simultaneously a philospher, linguist, semanticist, phonetician, physician, and so on. But the amount of skill and information we would have to master is simply beyond our powers.

So in spite of their best efforts, this group of specialists cannot

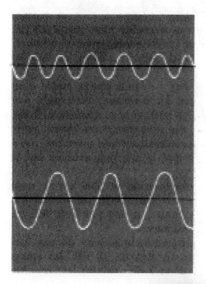

FIGURE 1. PURE SOUNDS

ABOVE: HIGH (PITCHED);
BELOW: LOW (PITCHED)

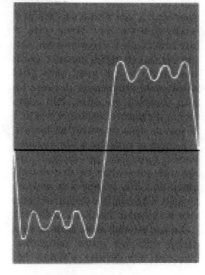

FIGURE 2. COMPLEX SOUND

THE WORD, THE ORIGIN AND THE FIRST MODULATION OF ALL RESONANCE.

attain a complete knowledge of language. The definitions are never more than partial views of the whole truth concerning the Word. Such definitions may satisfy the soul, but are quite inadequate from other points of view.

Man speaks. Speech is his most detailed, nuanced way to communicate and relate. It allows him to find himself, to become conscious of his own existence, and to better spot his limitations within his own life.

These concrete aspects can be seen and studied. The rest, especially the origins, will remain in darkness, wrapped in the deepest mystery of creation. The hope of finding the mother of all tongues is likewise, in our opinion, more of a dream than a real possibility.

The universal language is the linguist's burning desire. The myth is kept alive by the story of The Tower of Babel, but the reality is only to be found in the fact of speech. Language, as a mode of expression, is common to all men. This function represents the most extraordinary act for man and differentiates him from all other animals. Language must be recognized as the initial impetus that gave man the most effective, creative, and innovative tool he has ever possessed. The unity we seek exists in human language, constituted by the faculty of the Spoken Word. The use of this faculty has varied according to particular tendencies and resulted in the first breakup, which is the source of wide divergence. The starting point chosen was definitely critical. Adopting one or another mode entailed the risk of subjecting thought to a more or less favorable ideation process. Such differences distinguish the great linguistic groups; the character of a language binds to the internal conditioning it instills.

The variation within each group clearly shows the degree to which we are slaves of our environment; in addition, each individual exerts influence through his own unique mechanism of elaboration.

We insist and repeat that we are more or less consciously,

detectably, and inextricably chained to our environment, and most inescapably to the one medium in which we live: the air that surrounds us. It is essential not only because it is the breath of life, but also for its acoustic properties.

Rather than our tongue, mouth, or larynx, it is the air that is the instrument we use to speak. We invented very elaborate ways of acoustically agitating the surrounding air, which has acoustic properties of its own that beg to be exploited and which we have mastered. But we can only exploit what is there. The surrounding air presents certain qualities under certain conditions, varying according to physical factors such as location, climate, and humidity. Notice the feeling of euphoria in a reverberating environment, which makes you speak more loudly and even at times break into song, as opposed to the anxiety produced by the difficulty of emission in a dampened space. These are extreme cases, and the wide range of possible intermediates should not be ignored. Thus, a mixture of frequencies clearly examined and tallied as to its various components will be modified according to the medium in which it occurs. Given an identical source and a changing medium, the result will be different. This phenomenon is one of the main determinants of linguistic variation, primarily because as we adapt to our environment we are forced to mold our hearing to the acoustic conditions favored by such an environment. Our great adaptability allows us to refine our sensory utilization of the medium and, more important, to exploit the natural resonance of the medium for information. Where this adaptation cannot occur, the result is muteness or deafness or both.

After starting at the pinnacle where thought takes wing, we are back on Earth, faced with a mechanistic problem of sound resonance. Shot against real and solid supports, the Word will hopefully bounce like a ball back to the spheres where it belongs. No harm can come in this little incursion into the domain of matter; it is sufficient to recall the comments of the Zohar on *Genesis*:

It must not be concluded, from matter having been created by the Word, that the same had already manifested itself before the creation. Certainly, it exists for all eternity, but it only manifested itself for the first time when matter had been created ... Thus by a mystery of the most recondite, the infinite struck the void with the sound of the Word, even though sound waves are not transmissible in the void. The sound of the Word was hence the commencement of the materialization of the void. But this materialization would always have remained in an imponderable state if, at the moment it struck the void, the sound of the Word had not raised the sparking point, which was the origin of light that is the supreme mystery and whose essence is inconceivable.

Since, according to the *Book of Splendor,* the world of matter was born of the Word, it is normal that it should return to the Word, its origin. It is normal that any vibration, in striking the world of matter, cannot help but awaken the Word, the origin and first modulation of all resonance.

The Ear and Audition

DE VOCIS AUDITUSQUE ORGANIS HISTORIA ANATOMICA (1601).

■ The Listening Ear

At the beginning of time, the first human beings to find themselves suddenly scattered to the corners of the earth must have
lived "with their ears on alert." We assume this for the sake of discussion. We cannot go back any farther in our tale of the ear than
the phrase "long ago," and we must admit that this opener is a
convenient beginning to a past where reality, legend, and imagination intermingle.

Alertness was undoubtedly one of the first attitudes of the ear.
Surrounded by the steady noise of the first inhabited zones, the
ear must have turned toward any sound that was unusual or
indicative of the approach of prey or danger.

The initial role of the ear was probably that of an antenna,
whose long sensors constantly scanned the distance out of which
a potentially fatal event could arise at any moment. The ear
extended the body, so to speak, to the limits of its hearing range,
even when the other sensory antennas had unfavorable conditions. Alone among our radars, hearing was able to operate continuously, by day and night and in any weather.

The ear soon proved better adapted to this type of tactical
operation than sight, smell, or touch. The smallest hillock, fallen

branch, or tree-trunk in the way, and our visual field is blocked; fading light, a thin veil of fog, and our optical detection, perfect as it may be, loses effectiveness and range. It is the same for our sense of smell, degenerate to begin with, and easily confused by the lightest breeze. As for our tactile tentacle, as valuable as it is, it is the slowest in making us aware of danger.

The ear, which is our current concern, is thus our primary probing and checking weapon. More importantly its wide angle allows it to sweep over a large area and to determine with ease the direction of any sound therein.

Our image of *homo sapiens* crouching in a corner, on guard against a possible enemy, is more than likely too stylized. We probably overestimate the dangers to which he was exposed. Our imagined fright is only the residue of past ancestral phantoms and fantastic monsters that we would hate to meet.

We can consider man with his two ears as accessory defensive weapons but at the outset we find him submerged in a human element, if we are to believe Teilhard de Chardin. His way of life has largely surpassed the defensive attitude. His destiny turns him irresistibly toward a world where thought reigns supreme.

Man quickly breaks down the purely animal boundary in which his instincts are the masters; without surcease he invests his whole sensory capital into consciously informative goals, which he learns to memorize and to achieve by rapidly building a coordinated system. He uses his body as a perfected instrument that can exploit the Human that he is within the man that he is.

The sensorium evolves beyond its primordial activity. Where man once smelled, he now learns to scent; where he once saw, he now learns to look; where he once heard, he now learns to listen. He intellectualizes his senses. Everything contributes to his utilization of his inner creative force. He makes his body into a complex analytic instrument capable of seeing and following the path pointed out by the cosmic Intelligence, of which he is the human emanation.

■ The Ear and Its Evolution

Inquire about the ear and the neat question mark formed by its auricle will flash before you to suggest the enigma that lies beyond, one of the most arduous investigations you will ever face.

Anatomically, the ear is a most complex organ. In man, it attains an astonishing degree of perfection. We shall not launch into a detailed description of its labyrinthine structure. Let us simply say that audition is the act performed by a three-stage anatomical unit that comprises the following, beginning with the outside:

- The outer ear, which extends from the auricle or pinna to the tympanic membrane or eardrum.
- The middle ear, which contains the so-called "ossicles," a chain of three small bones termed "hammer," "anvil," and "stirrup" and found in that order. This chain is suspended by ligaments inside a cavity limited on one side by the tympanic membrane and on the other by the outer wall of the inner ear. In addition, two tiny muscles act respectively on the hammer and on the stirrup. The ossicles join the eardrum with the inner ear, the hammer literally penetrating the thickness of the eardrum with one of its extensions called the "handle," while the stirrup has its base, called "footplate," integral with one of the two membranes that seal the inner ear.
- The inner ear, which is the third stage, is the most complex in structure and is deservedly called the labyrinth. It comprises two organs: one called "vestibule" that does not interest us now, as it acts on position and balance; the other called "cochlea" that is specifically the organ of hearing.

With only this bare minimum at hand we could say that sound is collected by the outer ear and reaches the inner ear by crossing the ossicle bridge of hammer-anvil-stirrup. This over-simplified

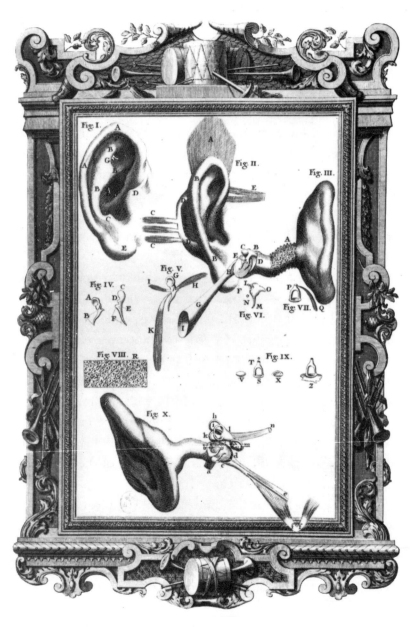

PHYSICA SACRA (1733).

theory fits in well with the minimally detailed structure we have sketched.

In fact, it will not be so easy to provide a precise explanation of the operation of the auditory apparatus. Without dwelling on it, we simply point out that its functional complexity is only matched in reality by its anatomical complexity.

It is essential for our purposes to know that no matter how simple or complicated the ear's mechanism actually is, it has become the organ that allows us to hear. Thus we deliberately mention only the functional unity of this assembly of conjoined bits and pieces. Information about the ear's evolution through an exceptional set of circumstances will assist the reader to understand the development of a functionally complex assembly that led man to construct his language with great perfection.

Two ways provide entry to this evolutionary path. Both allow us to appreciate how at various stages new functions appeared, true combinations that are often very complicated and cannot help but leave us wondering at the extravagant and magical genius that produced them.

We are talking about ontogenesis and phylogenesis. The first is concerned with purely embryonic evolution, while the second focuses on the family tree of the species. Though apparently unrelated, in fact these two research techniques complement and support one another.

At the end of the last century, Bonnier used this method of investigation to explore the physiology of the ear in ways that were very advanced for his time, despite his lack of access to advanced technical means. Here is what he writes in his *Traité sur l'oreille*:

To reduce an organ to its simplest expression, there is no more legitimate method than to retrace its whole ontogenesis, moving backward in time from the perfect and complete formation to the first embryonic rudiments.

...Phylogenesis alone offers a series of forms that no doubt are more or less regularly linked, but by which all components can be studied in full operation and through which they are designed to operate. Meanwhile, ontogenesis helps us to find in general organic forms, varied as they may be, the typical forms whose linkage parallels embryonic development, condensed and inexplicit, of the human organ under consideration.

...Comparative physiology and physiogenic sequencing lead us to a human physiology quite different from that which results from a direct study of the human organ. Analogy and induction allow a very deep penetration into the complexity of auricular functions.

Ontogenesis draws upon embryology for the laws governing individual development. Fritz Muller stated in a striking monograph that ontogenesis is merely the repetition of the paleontological progression of the species.

In addition, the embryology of the ear shows the progressive contribution of various forces in shaping this organic complex and the absence of initial unity. C. Eyries and B. Perles wrote on this subject while dealing with ear embryology in *Encyclopédie médico-chirurgicale*:

... A functionally and anatomically complex organ, the ear does not present any unity in its development. The inner, middle and outer ear differ both in the chronology of their formation and in the tissue from which they originate. All three of the elementary layers constituting the embryo at a very early stage participate in the formation of the ear. The superficial layer, or ectoblast, provides the membranous labyrinth and the cutaneous lining of the outer ear; the inner-most layer, or entoblast, is at the origin of the Eustachian tube and of the mucous membrane that lines the pneumatic cavities of the middle ear; the intermediate layer, or mesoblast, contributes the bony labyrinth, the ossicles, their muscles and the cartilage of the outer ear.

Finally we borrow a few passages from Robert Cordier and Albert Dalcq, who in Grassé's *Traité de Zoologie* bring our knowledge of the stato-acoustic organ up to date:

…Among the great sense organs present in the head of ver-tebrates there is one that solely perceives excitations of a mechanical order. Its role is to inform the organism both of the position the same occupies in space and of the displace-ments it undergoes, as well as of the vibrations that occur in the surrounding medium. This registration presupposes fun-damentally an ampule-like liquid-filled device, additionally an apparatus for transmitting external vibrations, and possi-bly a trumpet to improve reception. The acquisition of these organs has occurred over the course of evolution through a series of innovations, combinations, and readjustments whose curious stages are cooperatively revealed to us by comparative anatomy and embryology. The result of this progression at an orthogenetic pace, tinged however, with a singular touch of opportunism, has been the astonishingly perfected stato-acoustic organ of higher vertebrates. The human ear and all the consequences it involves from an intellectual and aesthetic viewpoint, thus appears as a com-plex whose analysis reaches to the heart of great biological problems.

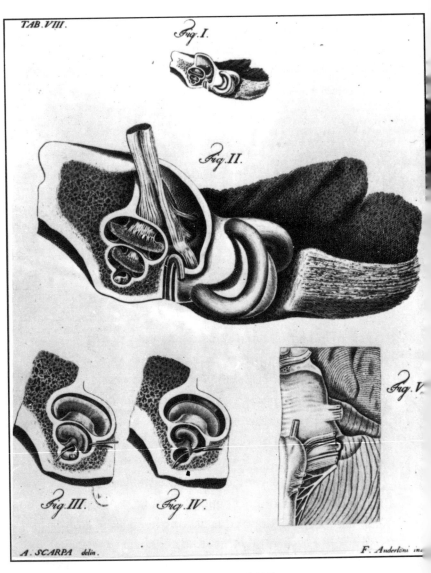

ANATOMICÆ DISQUISITIONES DE AUDITU ET OLFACTU (1789).

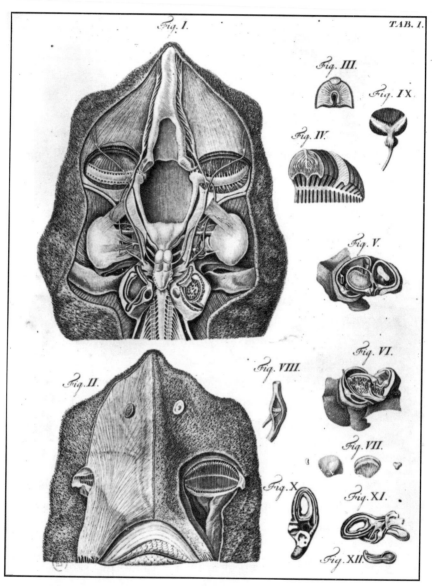

ANATOMICÆ DISQUISITIONES DE AUDITU ET OLFACTU (1789).

In their anatomical sketch these authors add:

>...The fundamental part present in all vertebrates is the labyrinth (internal ear of mammals).
>
>The latter is placed in the interior of a generally closed chamber, the auditory capsule, which in the lower vertebrates is formed of cartilaginous tissue. In some species it communicates more or less directly with the cranial cavity, to the point where substantial parts of the labyrinth, sometimes the whole organ (sea horse), are located inside the skull in contact with the brain.
>
>In higher vertebrates a bony girdle is formed around the labyrinth perfectly matching its contours. Thus can be described, on the one hand, a bony labyrinth that can sometimes be isolated without too much difficulty from the skeleton of the cranium and, on the other hand, a membranous labyrinth located inside the first.
>
>The membranous labyrinth is filled with a clear liquid, the endolymph; between its outer surface and the cartilaginous or bony case that envelops it exists a perilymphatic space, filled with perilymph and generally partitioned by fine conjunctive tissues. Even in the case where parts of the labyrinth are free in the cranial cavity, perilymphatic tissue still adheres to their outer surface. The auditory capsule in its simplest form is perforated by orifices providing passage for at least two formations: the fibers of the eighth nerve pair (VIII) and the endolymphatic duct.

Here is what they report in their evolutionary sketch:

>In the lower vertebrates with aquatic life (cyclostomi, fish), the labyrinth constitutes the only part of the stato-acoustic apparatus. From the amphibians, at the external side

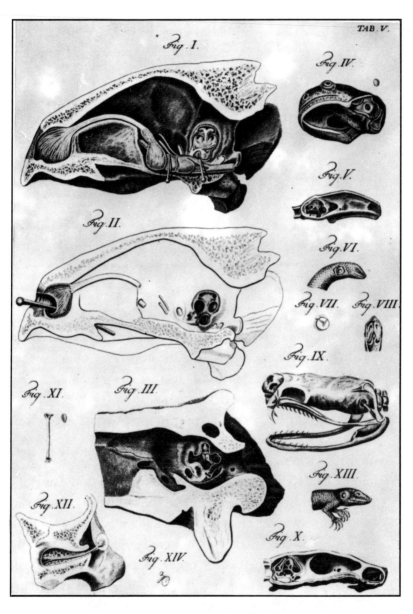

ANATOMICÆ DISQUISITIONES DE AUDITU ET OLFACTU (1789).

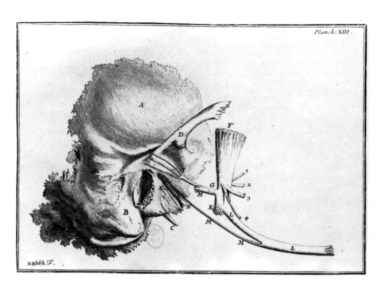

TREATMENT OF THE HEARING ORGAN (1731).

of the labyrinth, a new cavity appears that narrowly adapts to it. This cavity, the case of the eardrum, is none other than a transformation of the first branchial cleft (hyomandibular cleft) that has lost all free communication with the exterior but still maintains its continuity with the pharynx in the form of a more or less wide conduit, the Eustachian tube. A part of the skeleton of the hyoid arch is incorporated therewith, and in the form of a bony piece (the columella of the amphibians and sauropidae), the stirrup of the mammals adapts very exactly to a new orifice made in the auditory capsule (or bony labyrinth), whose orifice it completely closes, constituting the oval window. On the outside opposite the labyrinth, the tympanic cavity joins the skin and is closed by a membrane of reduced thickness, the eardrum.

Finally, in mammals and birds there is added to this complex a more or less deep invagination of the integument: the external auditory canal. Its inner end is represented by the eardrum, which is thus no longer at the surface; near its outer extremity mammals developed cutaneous appendages of various form and dimension that constitute the pinna. This assembly is called the outer ear, and the tympanic cavity is designated under the name of the middle ear, while the labyrinth is the inner ear.

It is preferable to study the evolution of the ear within the same species. Undoubtedly such a Darwinian study in man, for example, would throw new light on the evolution of the ear and, consequently, of audition, which would considerably influence the study of language.

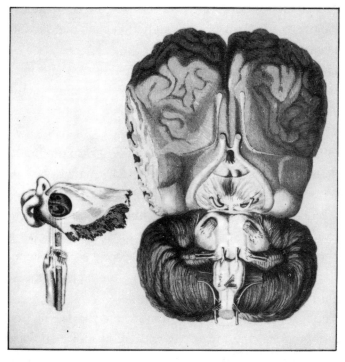

TREATMENT OF THE HEARING ORGAN (1731).

Such is the main evolutionary perspective of the ear. A more precise analysis of the development of the middle ear will increase our understanding of the functional unity required by the act of speech, which involves not only the ear but also the mouth, the pharynx, the larynx, and other body parts.

As mentioned above, the middle ear contains three ossicles, the hammer, the anvil, and the stirrup, listed in their order from the outside to the inside. They are embryologically of different origin and derive at the beginning of fetal development from completely different areas. Traces of this archaic structure will be found in mechanisms considered later.

The hammer and anvil are progressively shaped from a cartilage called "Meckel's cartilage," which supports the first of four branchial arches bordering on each side the cephalic extremity of the embryo. The stirrup is roughed out of the second arch by Reichert's cartilage.

It is important to remember this duality of origin in the formation of our auditory apparatus. It explains many reactive mechanisms we will later encounter.

The separate derivation of the ossicles, namely the hammer-anvil assembly on the one hand and the stirrup on the other hand, reveals why these are provided with a separate vasculature and independent innervation. This latter trait is to be underlined. The first block, the hammer-anvil assembly (also termed incudo-malleolary) is under the domination of the mandibular nerve belonging to the fifth cranial nerve, while the second (called stapedial, consisting of the stirrup) answers to the command of the seventh or facial nerve.

The first arch, or more exactly the anterior part of Meckel's cartilage, produces the lower jaw with all its muscular, vascular, and neural attributes. The second arch further extends the facial involvement of these embryonic elements. The synergy of facial expression, which is so functionally tied to the manner of hearing, finds therein one of its most solid ontogenetic foundations.

Though it would be fascinating to detail the organic progression all the way to the end of fetal life, our limited space restricts us to drawing only a few conclusions. On the scale we have selected, the mouth and the outer part of the middle ear form one group. More precisely, the face musculature, except for the eyelids and the stirrup with its muscle, form a single unit. In short, the total functional whole of the middle ear infers *ipso facto* a functional unity of mouth and face, better still of mouth, face, and ear.

■ The Ear and the Auditory Function

In auditory function, the ear is an entity capable of perceiving and analyzing acoustic pressure. In precision and speed of operation it defies the possibilities of any laboratory machine, no matter how advanced.

Though the ear's primary ontogenetic or phylogenetic purpose was to track down variations in pressure, as it evolved it went beyond perception and analysis of such variations. It could dissociate and sample the various parameters that constitute the sound, namely pitch, timbre, duration, and intensity.

Yet its highly differentiated activities only extend over a fairly limited range of sonic phenomena. Not all vibrations of the air, which is our vehicle of acoustic communication, have the same effect on the ear. The ear cannot absorb all these disturbances, and that may be for the best. The limits of its operation are well defined. On a frequency plane the ear's perception is confined by a lower threshold, below which are sounds too low to be heard (labeled "infrasonic"), and an upper threshold, above which are sounds that escape the ear and become inaudible (designated "ultrasonic"). Between these two limits lie the so-called "audible" sounds on a wide band ranging on the average from 16 to 20,000 cps. Cases of exceptional hearing do exist: some broadcasting professionals can clearly perceive up to 22,000 or 23,000 cps. One

CASES OF EXCEPTIONAL HEARING DO EXIST.

we tested several times could hear 27,000 cps.

All perception within this band is *not* of the same quality. Bass and treble extremes at the borders of our perception yield poor responses from our sensory organ. By contrast, the ear can analyze sounds to an often disconcerting degree and perfection in the band between 50 and 5,000 cps.

The high sensitivity band applies to all parameters under analysis. If one looks at curves representing sensitivity as a function of frequency, they produce a shape that, as Wegel noted, resembles a lemon. Figure 3 shows Wegel's Curve. In addition to indicating the high and low frequency limits, this diagram shows the minimum threshold level of human auditory perception (below which

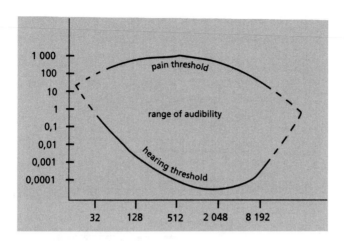

FIGURE 3. WEGEL'S CURVE

the ear hears only silence) and the level above which hearing becomes painful and intolerable.

Sensitivity to intensity is also analyzed by the ear. We perceive sounds as loud or faint according to their energy content. But this simple criterion is difficult to use because it lacks a defined unit of measurement. Therefore physicists and physiologists created a unit to value the audition of a sound and used it to establish norms for what is presumed to be normal hearing. Of course, whenever we try to define physiological normality we are on shaky ground, all the more so because the unit we have to adopt is a unit of sensation. How can one assert without qualification that a cup of coffee is twice or three times as sweet as another? Can the rigidity of the physicist be reconciled with the fantasy of the senses?

Derived from mating the work of Weber and Fechner, psychophysics proposes to measure sensation. In 1834 Weber formulated the principle that our body does not perceive a measurable variation of an external stimulus until it attains a certain increment in constant ratio with the preceding stimulus. This stimulus may, for example, be produced by an increase of weight, pressure, heat. When the variation of the stimuli begins to increase constantly in linear fashion, our perception is modified at recordable intervals. The distribution of these points is such that each is at a greater distance from the one that follows it than from the one that precedes it. The distribution is foreseeable and is thus measurable for each point. In other words, the variation of the stimulus is perceptible to us when for each of the values I of this stimulus the $\frac{\Delta I}{I}$ is constant.

This constant represents the quantity by which the intensity of stimulation has to increase in order to produce the perception of a sensory modification. This is known as the Law of Weber and is of key importance in the field of psychometry.

Fechner, to his credit, utilized these results and transcribed them in mathematical terms, so that it was possible to speak of sizes and define units of sensation.

In *Elemente der Psychophysik* in 1860, Fechner described his concept of how to measure sensation. He parted company with Weber's view that sensation only varies from point to point as a function of the continuous progression of the intensity of stimulation. Instead he concentrated on the linear and continuous variation of sensation in order to reveal the parallel progression of stimulation. He declared that sensation represents the sum total of all the increments perceived through the increasing variations of the stimulus; thus, sensation "S" becomes easily measurable and can be expressed by the formula:

$$S = \Sigma \, \frac{\Delta I}{I}$$

whereupon the curve of intensity variations takes the form of a geometric progression, a result that allowed him to write:

$$S = K \log. I$$

(K = constant proper to each type of sensory excitation).

Concerning the ear, increments of acoustic intensity resulting in a change in sensation are expressed in bel, or preferably in the more manageable decibel (the tenth part of a bel). The increment

of intensity is equal to the logarithm to the base 10 of the ratio of
the acoustic pressures.

$$(I o - I) \text{ bel} = \log. \frac{P}{Po}$$

or:

$$(I o - I) \text{ decibel} = 10 \log. \frac{P}{Po}.$$

An audiometer is used to measure auditory sensitivity. As a kind
of electronic pitch-pipe, it typically gives a dozen known frequencies for which each intensity progression can be read in decibels.

■ Summing Up

The main function of the ear and the justification for this book is
to absorb language with a particular predilection, tasting it,
appraising it, drawing off its substantial marrow, purifying it and
putting it away in the storehouses of the brain. Formerly on guard
against danger or on the alert for prey, the ear has now become
our window on the enigma of the world of sound, bearer of most
human communication.

   To reach that point, our ear underwent a long and patient
apprenticeship through various stages that repeat the process by
which we became human, through the pairing of man and language. Each person retraces the path of humanity as a whole. What
man does with word is to make a gift of himself. The spoken word
demands that he awaken to the awareness of his own existence.

   It is to language that he owes his introspection; it is through the
ear that his concentration begins to converge upon his self. It is
through hearing his own voice that the notion of life penetrates him.
It is by constant play with the word that he acquires a body image.

   The next chapter traces this long human training, the sum of
social conditioning he must undergo.

Audio-Vocal Conditioning

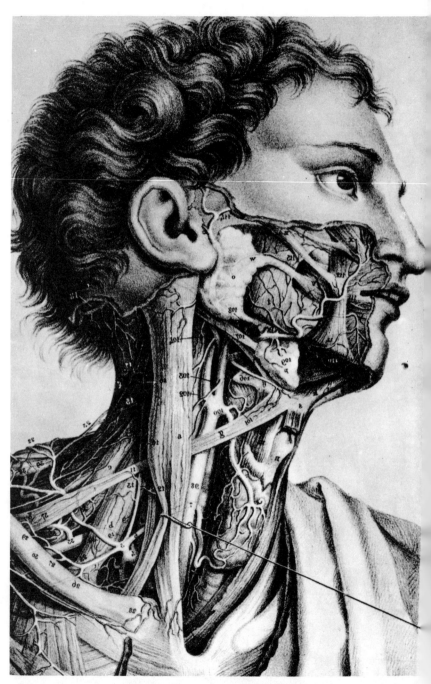

AMONG THE MOST EXTRAVAGANT SUCCESSES IN MAN'S HUMAN ADVENTURE IS THE
EXTRAORDINARILY HARMONIOUS COUPLING OF HEARING AND THE ORGANS OF SPEECH.

■ Origins of this Conditioning

Among the most extravagant successes in man's human adventure is the extraordinarily harmonious coupling of hearing and the organs of speech.

Originally a listening antenna capable of locating sounds, the ear gets into the game of analyzing and examining them at high speed. It discerns the various components of acoustic constructs better than our most advanced measuring instruments, especially taking into account how little time it has at its disposal to perform these operations.

The ear thus seems to forego its pure and simple role of sound locator in favor of being a rapidly scrutinizing sound analyzer. Since that conversion, the ear has intellectualized its listening methods.

We may unhesitantly view the ear as a sonic mouth. The same branchial organs form the middle ear and the oro-pharynx. The common motor and sensory origin is the source of the organic intimacy and functional unity of mouth and ear.

In man, spoken language forms an exceptionally advanced use of the resulting synergy of this neuromuscular conjunction. The suddenly opened ear had only to take a small step to toss out through the mouth what it just heard and digested. This auditory stage, the first that characterizes our awakening to life, begins to take form during uterine life.

Consider the well-known and extraordinary event with song birds, which is related by Negus in *The Mechanism of the Larynx*. If the eggs of songbirds are incubated by birds that do not sing, the birds hatched out of that brood also do not sing. For the auditory and phonic association to be formed, the acquisition of such a primitive bird language requires a permanent excitation of the neuro-muscular synergy that characterizes the functional organ of language.

Our laboratory work suggests the possibility of intra-uterine audition by the fetus. We supposed that in addition to the heartbeat the various sounds of speech had a good chance of penetrating the uterus and reaching the budding auditory apparatus. Recording through a liquid layer revealed what was likely to be heard by our freshman speaker. The results obtained on the magnetic tape are very agreeable to the ear. The sounds are similar to the noise of a waterfall, interspersed with all kinds of pleasing clickings. The child exposed to this audition incontestably takes great pleasure in it. Non-speaking but hearing children draw meaningful sensations from it because of their memory of a not yet remote past. The most striking effect is the extreme mobility of the face, which comes alive especially with the lips as they extend to suck.

Thus it seems possible that the fetus already participates in the sonic activity of the world it strives to enter. He enters it with a cry of distress. This desperate cry is testimony perhaps to our confusion, to the call of the paradise lost that is our mother's womb. Already the humans who surround us fail to understand. They listen, waiting for the first cry with anxiety, with joy. Yet it expresses our grief at being the victim of rejection. It is our first great contact with the air that surrounds us, so rich in the acoustic properties that we will learn to utilize.

Have we heard this cry of despair? Did it stamp us to the quick with an unknown pain? Do we already foresee what life in the open holds in store?

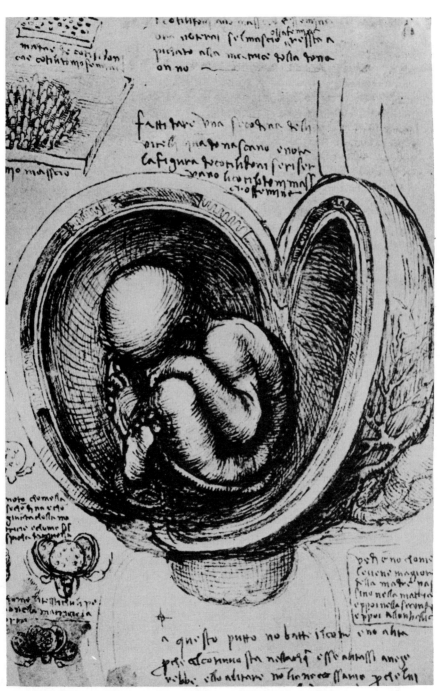

WE SUPPOSED THAT IN ADDITION TO THE HEARTBEAT THE VARIOUS SOUNDS OF SPEECH HAD A GOOD CHANCE OF PENETRATING THE UTERUS.

■ The Beginnings of Audio-Vocal Conditioning

Accustomed to uterine audition in a liquid medium, our ear must suddenly adapt to aerial noise. This will no doubt take time. Still, as soon as the "sonic labor" is over and we leave our aqueous medium to hear thereafter only through the layer of air, we begin to be cuddled and caressed by a voice that seems to be the same as the already familiar one that spoke to us in the depths of our uterine night. We think we recognize it, even though we cannot put an image to it. This voice approaches whenever we cry with hunger. As we suck with greed what our mouth has touched, we drink avidly at the same time of the voice that pours its bounty over us. Vocal food is as necessary to our human development as the milk we take in. All our cells have their required nutritional needs, but so does our budding psyche. The voice, for which we long as eagerly as the nipple and soon associate with our mother's face, brings on responses, tiny cries of joy or sorrow.

This stage, which Ombredane calls the affective stage of language, shortly makes way for the play stage. From then on we witness the flowering of audio-vocal conditioning. Suddenly, while we listen, while we call — maybe we are only exercising our vocal cords — we become conscious of an extraordinary possibility at hand: that of making noises. And what noises! High ones, low ones, sharp ones, flat ones, short ones, long ones, loud ones, soft ones. Here is a game that enters into our human apprenticeship long before the use of our feet. To call out, to answer oneself, to hear oneself call, to wonder at the sound to which one listens, to recognize one's ability to emit and control or, up to a point, to hear this emission, represents one of the most appealing games imaginable. This primordial stage is the most essential in conditioning the ear to listen, more exactly, to self-listen. The nascent awareness of our emission and of our own audition is of all human phenomena one of the most constant, most precious, and most worthy of protection. Knowledge of the world is knowledge of its sonority; better yet, we seem to acquire it through acquiring knowledge of our own voice. The dialogue takes hold rapidly and without mediator; to the adult who leans over the cradle, it may sound incoherent, but it is highly significant to the infant who awakens to his own sensations. This endless game of sonic interchange, this bath in a tub of noise that we can run and take without anybody's help, constitutes our first awakening to life, our first declaration of independence, our first awareness of the complex mastery of coordination we will achieve as we develop.

Nothing in fact is less physiological than speech, a human phenomenon beyond doubt, but for whose purposes no organ was physiologically designed. Nothing in the catalog of our anatomical parts was directly meant to be used in speech. We were given a digestive apparatus and a respiratory apparatus, but no specific oral-language apparatus. What ingenious adaptation and unlikely combination was needed to attain that goal! A first group of organs consisting of part of the digestive system (lips, mouth, palate, tongue, teeth) and a second group connected with the respiratory system (larynx, nostrils, lungs, diaphragm, thoracic cage) had to get together in order for us to produce sounds. This nomenclature is not meant to do more, for the moment, than to bring together all the organs that contribute to the creation of language.

Was it really necessary to expect man to be furnished with a purely phonic organ, selectively adapted to language? We do not think so. Rather, the truly acquired character of human language implies a deeper adaptation of man's whole organism.

This adaptation begins with the mouth-to-ear game which we know how to play from the moment of birth. In this golden age of language any interference will considerably prejudice the later structuring of the speech function.

The fundamental human phenomenon of that age is our early discovery of the marvelous agency that controls our incoherent cries and allows us to produce them, regulate them, and direct them. The ability to cry, to call out, to listen, to willfully make sounds for one's own benefit as one's own audience and window on life, is one of the most extraordinary humanizing mechanisms ever observed in the evolution of language.

Of course, the troubles of daily life are already before us; hunger pangs make us scream in spite of ourselves. At first unself-conscious, these cries soon set forth our discontent, and the tear-less shouts accompanying our anger already show us the bad side of life, which our self-directed cooing sometimes makes us forget.

The world, which stops at our fingertips, surrounds us with noise, some of which we add ourselves. This phenomenon is human. We intentionally use this term, meaning that the event is peculiar to man, as distinct from the animal line. It is true for all children of man and is a characteristic of our species. The impor-tant phase of constructing and controlling language development allows the progressive formation of an auto-controlled emission circuit. To make a sound is primarily to auto-control it; to fashion a sound or a cry is to imagine it as one would want it to be; to toss it into space and listen to it allows us to judge whether it rep-resents what we thought we were creating.

This effort continues by trial and error, by constant effort, through all of our waking moments. Life begins to be divided between sleep and the development of our autonomy. This autonomy, which man is long in earning, is witness to the extra-ordinary tenacity we devote to our own development.

■ Shaping of the Speech Function

The ear at birth is passively open to any noise: it now begins to taste sounds it has learned to conceive. It progressively self-trains to swallow only what it imagines and structures. Babble gains tex-ture, enchanting the family who anticipate at any moment the appearance of coherent speech.

OUR MOST AUTOMATIC ANIMAL MOVEMENT OF SUCKING SEEMS TO BE THE MOST PRECOCIOUS OF THOSE WHO FAIL TO TAKE INTO ACCOUNT OUR SONIC PRODUCTION.

However, speech is only play at this stage and has little importance. Our vocal gestures have no meaning yet. Our sonic know-how is still too precarious. We are a long way from modulating the breath that escapes us and that has barely been brought to life by giving it sound.

It will take many weeks and months to firmly establish the essentials of our self-controlling network. Only then will we be able to use it as a vehicle for our thoughts.

To sum up, though we lack a language, our first human apprenticeship progressively forms the speech function.

From our mature adult behavior we do not understand the infant's stages of development of his most perfect action, that of speech. Our endless questions about what infant language means and tries to express are but meaningless attempts to interpret what does not yet exist. Assuredly, the infant does not say anything. He has nothing to tell himself. He is only playing the most fascinating game he will ever find. He uses his acoustic pacifier to the utmost. No construction toy, no Lego set is more fun than what is offered him. To have a machine capable of emitting and even receiving sounds is a wonder! Furthermore, to be able to improve the mechanism so that it will produce the sound signal one wishes is stunning! Already the will begins to influence the involuntary action, and the game continues.

■ The First Words

The play goes on, certainly, though there is still a long way to go. Our motor function will have to be awakened and coordinated before we achieve our most advanced conditioned act, that of speech. At this stage, we are still at the mercy of body movements well beyond our control.

These movements are our masters until the day when our will intervenes. At first it is no more than a caprice of our young cerebral mechanism, but later it begins to block or knowingly route the automatic reactions. The game is won, or at least it is under way. We become master of our motor equipment through our will. Emanating from our creative power, this force humanizes us while our perception concurrently absorbs the environment until we identify with it.

For a long time, at least a few weeks, we have been able to raise our eyelids to allow the sensory organ beneath them to see. Our visual horizon is still very close, extending barely beyond our hands. It sometimes embraces a silhouette from which comes an already familiar voice that floods us with its breath and regularly feeds us the fluid essential to our cellular growth.

For a long time, too, we have been able to grasp everything that comes near our mouth. Our most automatic animal movement of sucking seems to be the most precocious if our sonic production is not taken into account.

Finally, and yet preceding anything, we can hear as well as produce sound. This soon to be controlled cry is carried by our breath, is superimposed on it, and is identified with it. As soon as our mouth opens, the cry is born and instinctively physiologically modulated. Tongue and palate dome move apart, then come together again when the mouth closes. The resulting sound is cut down but not interrupted, and the first "ma-ma-ma-ma..." flies out into space.

Looking mechanistically at the genesis of language may destroy parents' illusions that invest meaning and identification into those first long-awaited words. Yet this interpretation does not devalue the beauty of the transcendent structural development of human language.

The child realizes very quickly that producing this first verbal chain, "ma-ma-ma-ma," can by itself immediately bring joy and smiles to the face that dominates his visual sphere; he understands that this first acoustic modulation serves as a call, a summoning bell. The apprenticing human already completely under-

INFINITE PRECAUTIONS MUST SURROUND THE INFANT AT THIS STAGE.

stands the function of speech and its use. He or she is aware of the vocal act and its informative ability.

Man again comes forth to achieve human status. On his breath he bears language. With that one act he retraces the genesis of his humanity. He relives in a few weeks the millennia needed to build the complete, increasingly complex means of communication using language.

It is only the first word that counts. The rest is only play — a game of acoustic construction. Just let the lips form to suck and then relax, and "pa-pa-pa-pa" succeeds "ma-ma-ma-ma."

These two essential words are now born and soon invested by the parents as symbols of family members. They quickly label themselves with these two terms, thinking and wanting to believe that the child has meant to designate them. Man in this respect is more naive than the infant who lies before him.

Two words, and the verbal world is already built. The word, or more exactly, the speech sequence "ma-ma-ma-ma..." and "pa-pa-pa-pa...," has acquired a nearly universal meaning. Mother is designated the same way throughout much of the world. The "ma-ma" that is so closely associated with the act of sucking indicates the being that suckles us; the "pa-pa" is naturally addressed to the other person. From now on, the training over the next several weeks will be difficult. The infant will have to speak, to talk to himself, to practice continuously. Thus the moment a deep-felt call, a resonance arising within us, brings us out of a deep sleep, we begin to babble grandly, quickly, and without ever tiring, provided nothing hinders us.

Any discomfort, even a slight one, that disturbs this critical phase can have a catastrophic effect on the development of the most human of our acts. An illness that irritates or frightens us removes all the pleasure from our play with the verbal pacifier. A sorrow or worry appears, and we are vulnerable to having our development blocked. If our calls, the verbal signs we perhaps awkwardly but nonetheless effectively learned to direct, go unanswered, if the mother is absent, then the vocal acts lose their meaning, and the game loses its attraction. It recalls instead a painful memory of some presence no longer seen or the pleasant call of a voice no longer heard or caressing our body with the vibrant, warm, and airy blanket of a sound we loved to hear, to drink, to breathe.

Infinite precautions must surround the infant at this stage, if in the ever-increasing whirl of life he is not to lose or delay the acquisitions essential to his language development.

With every test following this moment, the infant develops this control relay through which he became conscious of his own voice. Earlier, he learned to make his arms move, using all his will to create order and discipline in movements that previously disobeyed him. In the same way, with greater difficulty, he now succeeds in shaping his verbal act by learning to articulate.

The first words out respond to anatomical cavity stimulation. The infant opens and closes his mouth with his lips in the sucking position, and "mama" is formed spontaneously. His lips stiffen a little and retract, and "papa" comes out. His lips spread apart the least bit, and "dada" or "tata" take shape. Thus his verbal repertoire rapidly gains a wealth of elements, which he repeats, modulates, and reverses in an infinite number of ways.

However, the history of the spoken word cannot be recreated; it would take a millenia of ancestral experience to retrace this path of language acquisition and development. No doubt the evolution of our thought would profit little and again get stuck, as it must have before, in solely looking for ingenious ways to permit expression.

Progress occurs more comfortably if the infant observes, accepts, and adopts his ancestral heritage as if it were simply normal and inborn knowledge. In reality the only inborn (and extraordinary!) quality is the ability to absorb and concentrate the knowledge of all humanity in ourselves during the first few months of life. Children today turn on the television set before they are two years old and point their fingers at airplanes flying across the sky. This is a breath-taking abridgement of human history.

Just as we have found a structural phylogenetic progression of human anatomy, another exists for knowledge. The phylogenesis of knowledge allows our thought to take off from an ever higher and higher springboard placed such that we more easily fly into the upper reaches of the spirit.

Our verbal impetus comes from the outside; that voice we love to hear and listen to is our acoustic beverage. We would like to imitate it, but every time we try, some demon still makes us double the sound image we want to reproduce, as if it was impossible for us to shape and stick to a single group. Everything comes out double, as if repeated by a senseless echo. It is a curious occurrence, and certainly a bothersome one. We feel as if we cannot help behaving like the dog, who always barks back to the distant call of another dog. A cerebral echo (a sort of echolalia) comes out that cannot be dampened.

Perhaps we are not yet conscious of this automatic repetition — or at least of the disturbance it creates in our barely informative expression. Whatever the case may be, for a long time our vocabulary consists entirely of double expressions, such as "mama," "papa," "pepe," "popo," "dada," "dodo," "caca." After we learn to correct this fault of repetition by blocking it voluntarily through concentration, we keep in our linguistic storehouse only those words used that hold special significance, such as "mama" and "papa." The others remain infantile words.

The ability to hear oneself gives rise to the ability to listen to oneself, which in turn creates the faculty of speech. We are ready to analyze the workings of this ability to hear oneself.

Audiophonology

THIS SELF-DIRECTED LISTENING DEPENDS MAINLY ON OUR SENSE OF HEARING.

And he...put his fingers into his
ears...and saith unto him,
"Ephphata," that is,
"Be opened."

And straightaway his ears were opened,
and his tongue was loosed,
and he spake plain.
MARK, VII, 31-37
RECOVERY OF THE DEAF STUTTERER

■ Audition and Cybernetics

To hear, and to hear oneself. To listen, and to listen to oneself. This is the stage we have reached in developing our auditory conditioning to language. It sums up in the best possible way what is meant by "audiophonology." To "hear oneself speak" is the quickest and most concise definition of audiophonology.

The reader may ask why it was necessary to go on and on as we did, only to establish a concept that, like Columbus's egg, stands alone without any assistance. If we speak, it is because we hear. It is common sense to observe that deafmutes do not say anything because they do not hear anything: no mystery exists in this very obvious fact. It may seem useless to even broach the subject, much less to dwell on it; yet the more self-evident a fact, the more interesting it can be to re-examine the evidence. It often conceals the most unexpected riddles. Rather than to rediscover the evidence, our purpose is to re-emphasize its truth.

To speak is to listen to oneself. What does this milestone definition imply? It means that the one who speaks is the first to listen. The speaker is the first listener of his voiced language. He is the informant and the first to be informed. He benefits before anyone else by what he formulates.

Why does he need this information? It allows him to recognize and measure the intensity of his verbal flow. It makes him aware of all the inherent elements of his listening habits and voice quality. Finally, it ensures that his discourse will have continuity within the parameters of his speech. By listening to himself, the speaker knows that he is speaking, recognizes himself, and evaluates the speech volume required at any time. Moreover, he can appreciate the semantic value; in other words, by this process of continual self-listening, he is able to recognize the quality of information that he wants to inject into his discourse at any given time.

This self-directed listening depends mainly on our sense of hearing, often referred to in this book simply as *the ear*. The ear then becomes the main organ of control for our outwardly directed vocal information, for our language, in short. The ear is thus comparable to the regulator of a system that is both subject to and independent of it. More precisely there is an interdependence that is more than a simple association. It is a symbiosis of two functions, reliant on and indispensable to each other.

This subordination of functions, this regulation evokes a feedback circuit that starts with the ear as a receiver, to rule the output of the mouth within precisely defined limits.

If we grant to the ear the attribute of being a receiver that adjusts, governs, and steers phonation, we can envisage the audition-phonation complex as a marvelously apt demonstration of the theory of information and communication. Using the example of the ear as a model, we can easily approach an understanding of cybernetics.

The functional diagram of a self-regulating circuit, reduced to

FIGURE 4. AUTO-REGULATED CIRCUIT.

its simplest terms, consists of a line joining a first point, called *input*, to a second point generally called *output*, with a *feedback* shunt along the line.

The regulating effect depends entirely on feedback. In such a system the force influx, energy flow, load variation, and any other imaginable or desirable factors are stabilized between limits allowed by the receiver connected to the feedback.

The receiver continuously puts out instructions, which feedback returns to the input. These instructions direct and can exert a certain control over the input information load according to the tolerances in the programming of the *input-output* complex. In every system having a predetermined threshold and ceiling zone, any known output value corresponds to a known input value, and vice versa. The presence of the receiver and its feedback line balances these parallel functions.

In such a system the receiver has a certain actual or potential autonomy, provided it is itself connected to a setup that supports it and feeds it energy.

What occurs is true functional symbiosis. The receiver operates within its own species' limits, which determine the regulating parameters it can safely exercise. These parameters depend on

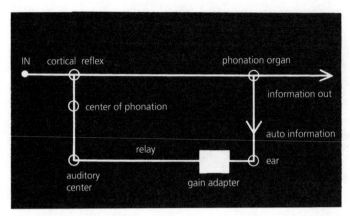

FIGURE 5. AUDIO VOCAL CIRCUIT

characteristics of the receiver: the time it takes to start working, the efficiency of its response, and how well it analyzes error or margin of tolerance. The mechanical complexity of such a regulating system is considerable, although we have intentionally reduced it to the simplest terms possible. Stripped of all mathematical formulation, here is a general sketch of the various ways in which our auditory receiver controls phonation.

- The auditory receiver is capable of hearing sounds within a certain band of frequencies, extending between 16 and 20,000 Hz.
- Out of this broad frequency spectrum it can choose certain bandwidths, on which it concentrates its selectivity and its affinity. The receiver thereby determines the quality of the load and imposes on it the bandwidth of its choice.
- In addition to this frequency control, intensity is regulated. We speak more or less loudly according to the sensitivity of our auditory mechanism to the acoustic intensities.
- One other element is introduced by the receiver into the feedback, which, when the cybernetic circuit is added into the preceding ones, is known as the "gain." This element is time.

The role of time is the hardest one to grasp, because it is the most confusing and disconcerting. This factor implies an element that is the reverse of the time taken to perform the act moving toward the output. It is a kind of recall, a memory, of the act as previously conceived. This verified memory is in charge of shaping the act to be, without hobbling it in any way by its intervention. The memory must operate in such a way that its role switches back and forth at all times between acceleration and braking, and in such a way that these opposite reactions are judiciously combined.

Though we could go on forever on this subject, we would be in danger of losing touch with the experimental investigation that alone can set guidelines capable of leading those who want to follow in cybernetic research.

■ Audiophonology and the Laboratory

Audiophonology is a recent creation, resulting from the consolidation of laboratory results collected between 1946 and 1951.

Our experimentation had two main goals, both arising out of our professional activity.

One, originating in statistical work on occupational deafness, involved the objective detection of faked hearing deficiencies. The other took shape in response to the needs of our clientele, which consisted at the time mainly of professional singers.

The questions we sought to answer in these two fields were:

• How do we hear?
• How do we sing?

Fortunately, we were soon able to establish through experimentation — though it did take a number of years — that the two problems were one and the same. All phonation was dependent on audition, and the latter was in part functionally supported by phonation. Our study of audio-phonatory reactions comprised several stages.

During the first period we discovered that in general no real correspondence exists between the classical anatomical description and the vocal qualities to be expected in a singer. A big larynx might produce a thin voice, while a tiny one might show the promise of a Wagnerian voice. Furthermore, some apparently damaged larynxes emitted exceptional sounds, while others, strictly normal or even exceptional from the anatomical standpoint, gave no indication in their acoustic activity of an ability to create a quality sound.

Second, from 1947 we tried without success to cure one of the best-known professionals of a fault in pitch, starting at E-flat above middle C, which had haunted him throughout his long career. We came to the conclusion that his larynx, which we had treated with various methods, was definitely not responsible for the lack of tonal precision in his emission.

The larynx had been the focus of our attention because we believed that any sound emission had to be tied to the vocal cords, and we had subjected it to examination with the laryngoscope. But if the larynx was not the root of the problem, what was? Where else could we look for a mode of pitch control? We directed our investigations to the ear.

■ Occupational Deafness in Singers

The first result we obtained was completely unexpected. We made the systematic discovery that singers are in danger of a kind of occupational deafness whose progress is observed to be the same as in our subjects exposed to the noise of piston or jet engines. This finding came as a complete surprise. We were so far from imagining that a singer could emit sounds of enough intensity to traumatize his own ear that we decided to take systematic measurements of the sonic energy involved. Again, the results were surprising: readings such as 100, 110, 120, 130 decibel (db); were easily reached with a sound level meter placed at a one meter distance. These are considerable intensities, which we had expected to find only in noisy boiler works or riveting shops near piston engines of 2,000 to 3,000 horsepower (hp), or in the vicinity of jet engines.

The research adventure we had embarked on proved so fertile, yet so disconcerting, that we were often forced to proceed by huge leaps, going from the incomprehensible to the utterly unexpected.

Looking back, we find it hard to conceive of how completely disconnected the islands of research seemed at the time. The synthesis of various elements requires such coherence that everything looks obvious to us now. After the first fifteen years of our work, the obvious logic of the system assured us that our investigations were valid.

From the very beginning our greatest obstacle to progress lay in the difficulty of freeing ourselves from our own prejudice — what we had learned and what was inbred in us. We could not conceive at the time that it would be so easy to lead a subject, not by the nose, but by the ear. It is hard to accept that we are so deeply indebted to a sense such as the sense of hearing, hard to comprehend that our voice, our inflexions, our timbre, in short, a great part of our being, depends essentially on our constantly listening auditory receiver. We carry within us, as part of ourselves, an indiscreet guardian who is unceasingly watching. Because this self-enslavement seemed so far outside the limits of our purely oto-rhino-laryngological training, for years we contented ourselves with collecting results without drawing conclusions, for fear that any conclusions might be shaky and premature.

Thus the only fact we took to be a certainty was that the noise emitted by a singer was destructive to his ear and that his professional life depended entirely on the soundness of his hearing.

This occupational deafness, which is identical to any traumatic deafness engendered by noise, is characterized by a break in the auditory curve, whose frequency spectrum is reduced by loss of sensitivity to high pitched sounds — the first manifestation being the appearance of a deaf spot (called a scotoma) at the level of 4,000 Hz. This impairment, which in the beginning stages is sometimes discovered only by accident, lies pretty high in the tone scale, and corresponds to C above the C of flutes, i.e., two octaves above C of tenor. This high-frequency defect would be of no consequence in itself, but it is soon accompanied by alteration of higher and lower frequencies, causing a spread in the loss of high-pitch sensitivity. If the defect produces a scotoma approaching 2,000 Hz, i.e., C of flute, the singer's voice becomes more frail, flat, and hesitant and less rich in harmonics. If the scotoma continues to invade the frequency spectrum and to erase control of the frequencies between 1,000 and 2,000 Hz, difficulties of tonal control result, and the vocal pitch is thereby compromised. The finest and most essential elements of song are altered, the ones that rule quality and that perceives pitch.

These findings — resulting from numerous systematic hearing examinations over a period of several years — led us to carry out some counter-experiments in the laboratory to solve the following problems:

1. To establish that phonation in singing depends on audition, and on audition only.
2. To determine that the zones of occupational deafness had isolated functions, in particular, those of quality control and pitch control.

The experiments below were carried out to this end:

1. By means of saturation we can partially manage to eliminate audition in the control circuit. To produce saturation it is sufficient to place the subject in an environment of high sound intensity, for

example, 100 db, for a period varying between 20 seconds and one minute. The sensitivity curve is strongly affected and the control is also disturbed. The subject can no longer sing satisfactorily. It is amazing to witness this test. The acquired technique of the singer suddenly and completely dissolves. In a flash nothing is left of his knowledge, his sensations, his control. The very image of the voice has been altered. This lapse of faculties stuns even the most forewarned experimenter. The long years of study and training and the subtle, skilled control techniques that singers use to guide the voice, manipulate the sound, and master their phonation, all of this vanishes. Nothing can help them to regain it. This spectacular crash of a habit leaves both the experimenter and the subject out of breath.

As soon as the ear recovers from the saturation, singing regains its brilliance. The technical control takes over once again. This experiment can be endlessly repeated with no change in the results. No surprise element is involved. The fact that no habituation is ever developed proves beyond contradiction the close dependence of phonation on the quality of audition.

2. It was difficult to use the same procedure, that of saturation, for a closer study of specific zones of interest. We wanted to learn the phonological disturbances that might arise by eliminating audition in various zones: above 4,000 Hz, between 2,000 and 4,000, then between 1,000 and 2,000, and finally between 500 and 1,000 Hz.

Due to the properties of the ear, partial saturation is impossible because saturation is a response to ear fatigue. Whatever practical tests are carried out (and there are many), and whether they are carried out with complex sounds or pure sounds, the consequences are the same: the whole sensitivity curve of the ear completely crashes. The results of the experiments are identical: they show a scotoma starting around 4,000 Hz, with only minor exceptions, whatever frequency is used. Thus we were led to use another

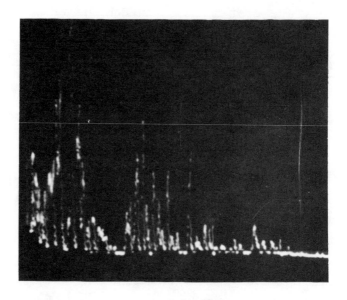

FIGURE 6 AND 7. PHONGRAM OBTAINED AFTER THE EMISSION OF A SENTENCE IN WHICH
THE TONAL RESPONSE CURVE IS EXPRESSED IN THE AUDIOGRAM BELOW.

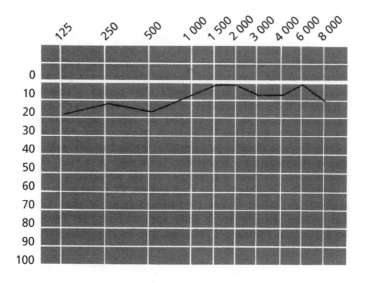

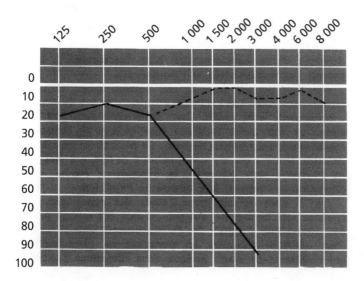

FIGURE 8 AND 9. PHONOGRAM RESPONDING TO THE SAME SENTENCE, EMITTED BY THE SAME SUBJECT, WHEN A FILTER IMPOSES ANOTHER RESPONSE CURVE ON THE AUDITORY SELF-CONTROL.

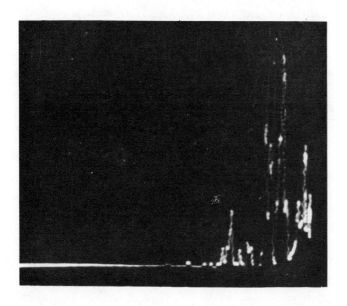

technique, consisting of eliminating one or another selected auditory band by introducing electronic filters into the auto-control circuit.

The filters have the effect of suppressing the bands we have chosen to eliminate from the auditory field. Their ease of handling makes it possible to work on any zone of audition without damaging the subject's hearing.

The technique is as follows: a microphone placed in front of the singer is connected to a linear amplifier. Next is a filter allowing truncation at will of the amplifier response curve, which is simultaneously picked up by a pair of earphones and returned to the singer's ears.

With this experimental setup it is conclusively proved that:

1. If the band above 2,000 Hz is truncated, the voice becomes colorless, stripped of its harmonic richness, more frail, guttural, and without resonance, especially when rising. Pitch is conserved, but apparently only the quality changes.
2. If only the band between 1,000 and 2,000 Hz is eliminated, the rest being left unchanged, the voice retains its original quality and richness, but the control of tonal level disappears. Singing on pitch becomes impossible.
3. If the zone between 500 and 1,000 Hz is modified in turn, it is then the accurate appreciation of total pitch that is altered. The subject is suddenly incapable of judging the pitch of any music played for him. At the same time his musical affinity becomes dulled.
4. If the whole curve is altered in the zone comprised between 500 and 2,000 Hz, the result is unmusicality.

This experiment is easily repeated and cannot be too highly recommended for demonstrating to what degree we are subject to the whim of our auditory master. A finer analysis shows that the disturbances that are introduced can be very slight. A very few decibels are often sufficient to cause considerable manifestations of disorganization in a long-established system. We can see a smile play on the lips of many learned readers who manipulate decibels and who are tempted to deny, or at least hesitate to admit, that a few decibels, 5 or 10 db at the most, can cause trouble as far-reaching as the destruction of an elaborate act developed through long training. Yet no particle of sand in a motor can compare in its effect with this apparently small deficit, whose logarithmic notation is sufficient to remind us forcibly that two sounds differing by 3 db are distinguishable, in that one is double the other, and that a sound 10 db louder than another is ten times as loud.

Our attitude was the same at the beginning of our research. We know full well that trying to persuade others of this finding risks pushing some people into rigid and unfounded opposition. We ask instead that they repeat our experiments, observe, and describe the results with the same strictness.

■ The Musical Ear

Having learned that auditory frequency band loss involves a concurrent suppression of fundamental characteristics of the singing or musical voice, we decided to investigate to determine the conditions under which an ear would be endowed with exceptional musical talent.

We systematically examined audiograms of musicians, that is, subjects who loved and were able to reproduce high-quality music. From these we defined the average auditory curve profile that would allow a gifted person to enjoy music coming from the outside and satisfying the conditions of good quality reproduction.

This curve always has the same profile, which may be described as follows: a curve ascends between 500 Hz (C above middle C) and 4,000 Hz (C four octaves above middle C) with a slope that varies between 6 and 18 db per octave up to 2,000 Hz. The curve is regular, without break or scotoma. The greater the slope, the more accentuated are the musical faculties.

From 2,000 to 4,000 Hz we note a dome curve, with a slight drop from 4,000 toward 6,000 Hz. If the same audiometric techniques and the same material are used, we know of no exceptions to this pattern. Anyone with a listening curve such as we have defined is

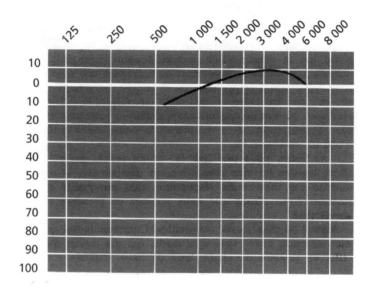

FIGURE 10. RESPONSE CURVE OF A "MUSICAL" EAR

certainly musical. The register in which he works also responds to his auditory receiver. The register depends on the band width for which he has affinity and within which he possesses the highest sensitivity to tonal variation and the greatest selectivity.

This typical curve ensures vocal pitch and quality. Others correspond to various auditory receivers of different characteristics, which operate under the following modes of control:

1. If the typical curve, taken as a model, is robbed of its treble beyond 2,000 Hz, tonal reproduction is still assured, but difficulties are experienced in the regulation of quality.

2. If the slope stops rising between 1,000 and 2,000 Hz, tonal reproduction becomes impossible. Pitch is faulty — yet affinity to music persists, bound to the presence of the ascending curve between 500 and 1,000 Hz. In this case only musical receptivity is realized. Faulty pitch does not exclude the appreciation of quality if the dome between 2,000 and 6,000 Hz is retained.

3. If the tonal curve takes a linear form or is completely disjointed, the reproduction is absolutely impossible both in quality and pitch. We would say that we are in the presence of an unmusical ear.

Thus we sing with our ears! How many times have we heard this absurd statement, which, where singing is concerned, always has the effect of silencing us.

■ Vocal Scotoma — Auditory Scotoma

Vocal modifications resulting from disturbed hearing require a more detailed analysis. Photographing the vocal images on a cathode ray tube revealed to us the harmonic qualities of sounds. Such an apparatus, termed a spectrum analyzer, can break down sound just as a prism can disperse light into a rainbow-like spectrum. It is possible to capture a sound, project it on a cathode ray tube, and study its various elements. Technical advancements made available more complex and precise setups, called panoramic spectrum analyzers. These translate various frequencies of sounds into quantitative visual images showing the relative values of each frequency. These sound spectrographs use a special paper impregnated with gunpowder to provide even more complete images. A needle becomes red hot when a frequency is present in the emitted sound and inscribes on the paper the various frequency, intensity, and duration characteristics of a phrase of 2.4 seconds duration. It is possible to section this image at some desired level in

PANORAMIC SPECTURM ANALYZER.

order to reveal the quantitative values of the intrinsic elements. The spectrum analyzer sections behave somewhat like instantaneous pieces of a speech sequence phrase, while cathode ray tube analysis of the same phrase (with the panoramic spectrum analyzer) allows us to obtain the envelope curve of the phrase. The envelope curve is in fact merely the integration of the various sections. This last procedure is the only one we used at the beginning and gives a wealth of results, which we will describe later.

More detailed analyzers are available, which are capable of examining sound close to a specific frequency. Better still, seven simultaneous channels make it possible to grasp the various parameters and to obtain all the spectrum characteristics. But we cannot resist raising a serious objection to all of these very capable apparatuses: they cannot reconcile precision and time. The more precise they are, the more time they require for analysis; the more advanced they are, the more cumbersome they become.

We have thus reached the point of talking of voice photography, by which we mean oscillograms, spectrum analysis displays and sound spectrograms. Whatever has influenced audition now can be read in our curves. The most striking phenomenon is the constant parallelism that ties together audition and phonation. Any change that happens to hearing is transmitted to the emission. When a filter of known band width is introduced to audition, a vocal frequential hole is translated to the emission shown on the cathode ray tube. The hole corresponds to the auditory scotoma imposed by the filter.

The parallel between audition and phonation is so constant that we can formulate it as a law, which is perhaps too bold — but it refers to a simple, basic fact: *the voice reproduces only what the ear hears.* In other words, a subject can only enact with certainty what he is able to control.

Here again, the facts seemed self-evident, but we took this rule to the laboratory for confirmation. In effect, while the subject can only emit all that he hears, he does not emit all that he hears for several reasons. First, our phonatory mechanism is limited simply through functional ineptness and cannot reproduce all the sounds that the human ear can detect, notably the extreme high pitches. Another qualification is that traditional hearing tests require an additional examination to search for the preferential listening band peculiar to each individual at any given moment.

This offers one of the most valuable objective techniques to be utilized in audition research, and we are convinced that a deeper study of the various parameters of voice will take us there in a simple and satisfying manner.

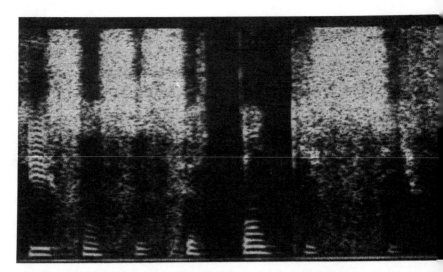

FIGURE 11. SONOGRAM OF THE SENTENCE "POUR QUI SONT CES SERPENTS QUI SIFFIENT." READ B HORIZONTALLY: TIME (2.4 SECONDS) — VERTICALLY: FREQUENCIES (0-8000 HERTZ); BY DENSITY: THE RELATIVE INTENSITIES OF THESE FREQUENCIES.

Certain that vocal emission in the laboratory could tell us a subject's way of hearing, we set out to detect the frequency bands of various human voices.

At the start we directed our attention to singers' voices. We repeatedly performed analyses of held tones and lengthy sung phrases to trace the envelope curves specific to each singer tested. Privileged zones clearly stand out in their spectrum analysis displays. Tight frequency bundles project with astonishing richness from the fundamental sounds, which excite the resonating cavities. The easily determined preferential zones immediately makes us certain of a particularly acute auditory control of the same preference. By drawing a few simple conclusions from these experiments, we were able to learn more about the mechanism which initiates the sound, namely, the ear.

The term "ear" designates the whole auditory complex, without prejudice as to the location of the functions on which our control characteristics are based. The ear, as conceived in our mind, extends from the external "ear" we can all see to its cerebral projection, which we cannot see.

Here we are in the midst of the deepest of mysteries. No matter, for the facts exist and cannot be denied. Let everyone interpret them in their own way. We can only justifiably dispute them through our own individual interpretations that any one of us may wish to make.

■ Conditioning to Singing

As we went on we made guesses at the way in which Caruso, Tita Rufo, Benjamino Gigli and many others heard. We tried to build listening devices allowing us to perceive sounds comparable to those heard by outstanding singers at the moment they were made.

This painstaking work enabled us to develop electronic setups capable of recreating at will auto-control modes that were identical to those of our experimental subject. These experiments quickly revealed their importance. A subject's emission changes the instant his auto-control, namely the capacity of his receiver, is modified; the emission improves exactly in the same areas as those that are auditively supplied. The subject's timbre comes to life and displays a spectrum analysis identical to the chosen model.

The phonological mechanism adapts itself technically to that found in the singer of the desired type. For example, the imposition of a Gigli-type control produces very forward phonation at lip level, automatically *mezza voce*; the lips stretch as in a pout, the nose becomes pinched at the base; the head is slightly deflected; respiration becomes deep and abdominal; and breath flow becomes regular and slows down noticeably. The singing manner can be profoundly altered and become identical with Gigli's. Of course, singing requires more than that; the quality remains specific to each individual. It is the same with singers as it is with instruments — some are by Stradivarius, while others are violins of lesser quality. It is interesting that in all subjects submitted to the experiment, the modus operandi of the whole

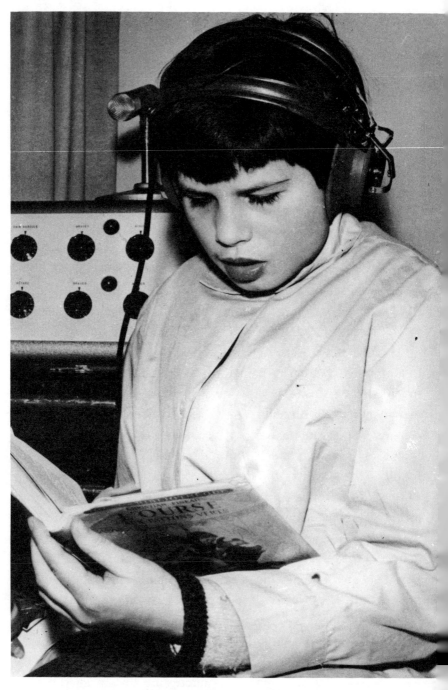

WE NEEDED TO BUILD A MACHINE THAT WOULD ALLOW ANY POTENTIAL SINGER TO LISTEN TO HIMSELF IN THE SAME WAY AS A PROFESSIONAL SINGER WOULD DO.

pneumo-phonological complex acts in a way that is, in every detail, similar to the methods used by the great masters.

The experience lasts for the duration of the experiment and then ends and vanishes. The great ease the subject experienced under the laboratory conditions leaves him with nothing but regrets! We therefore asked ourselves if it might be possible to develop therapeutic or educational methods to condition the subject to regain spontaneously such auditory modes whenever one so desired.

To this end we needed to build a machine that would allow any potential singer to listen to himself in the same way as a professional singer would do. Singing would thus become a conditioning to self-listening of emitted sounds responding to well-defined characteristics of the auditory receiver.

The development of these educational machines took a long time and involved several stages. In the beginning the participant used a manually controlled switching maneuver during emission. He would start with an auto-control mode which fed back to him exactly what he was producing in an unmodified form, and then accede to the desired manner of hearing whenever he wanted to emit a sound. Simple as it is, this system is difficult to operate. When electronic gates became available, we could provide a truly automatic passage from one to the other "ear" — in other words, going from the individual auditory channel, to opening the "song" channel whenever a sound was formed. The advantage of this system, operating without the knowledge of the subject, is that the conditioning is truly unconscious. Automatic reproduction is rapidly acquired. The time needed differs from one subject to another but generally involves half-hour education sessions every two days, over a period of one to three months, depending on retention and progress of auditory memories.

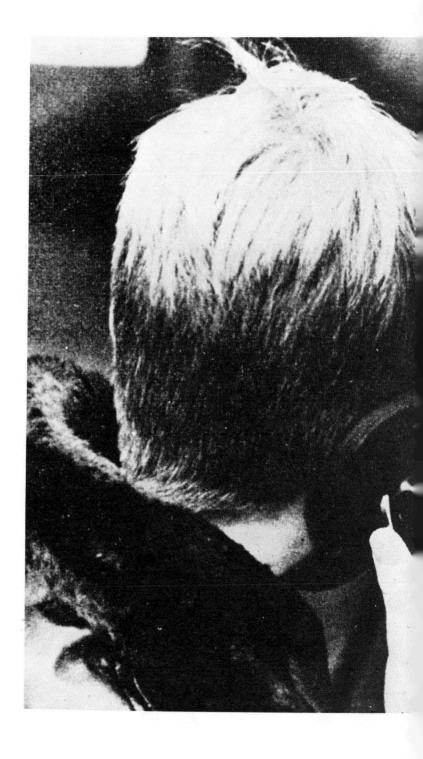

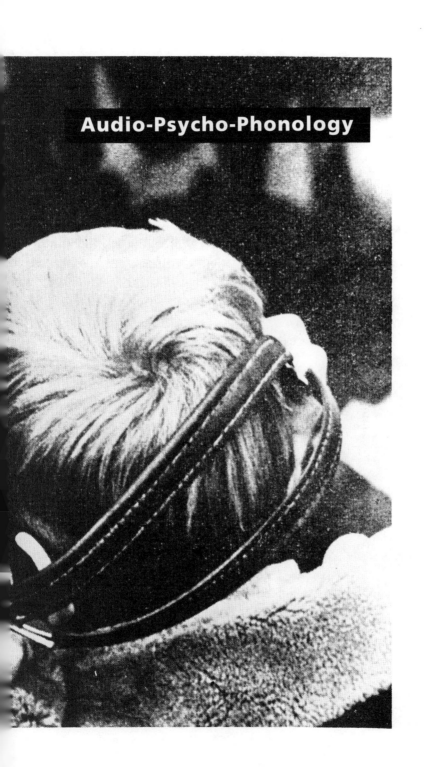

Audio-Psycho-Phonology

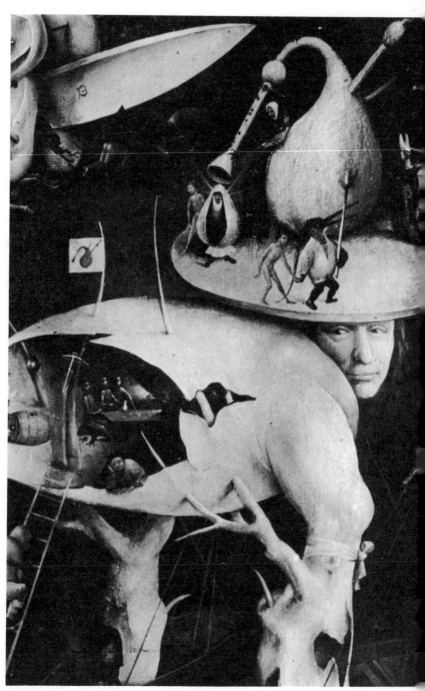

EAR, DOOR OF MY VOICE THAT PERSUADED YOU...

Ear, door of my voice that persuaded you,
I love you, you who gave a meaning
to the image by way of the idea.
APOLLINAIRE, THE NINE DOORS OF THE BODY

■ Conditioning to Language

Song is a means of expression that in many ways is related to spoken language. Thus one can reasonably approach the problem of language with the same techniques.

Is a poor voice caused solely by insufficient or defective auditory auto-control? Could the difficulties of emission generally grouped under the term dysphonia, such as harsh, raucous, and timbreless voices, be tied in with dysharmony in self-listening? Is there not a chance that articulatory difficulties in the production of speech, or dysarthria, might also be no more than the accurate reflection of an even more defective response of the receiver? Could the appearance of emission problems be explained by obscure causes — not necessarily grounded in a pathology such as otitis or tubal catarrh — that might interrupt the delicate and fragile audio-vocal conditioning process, definite evidence of the non-birth of a grandly elaborate adaptation, necessary to the flowering of our human role — so richly shored up by verbal support.

These possible underlying reasons eluded us for a long time. The response curves gathered for us by the audiometer were supposed to provide answers; but instead of helping us to solve the problem, they made the results obtained by comparative voice studies even more incomprehensible. The acoustic frequency bundles on emission were inscribed in the auditory range, but with such concentration at a certain level that at first we found it impossible to believe that any ear could be so functionally blocked to verbal use. We finally had to resign ourselves to believing it after we concluded our systematic research on the selective qualities of audition. In effect, the auditory field includes preferential, elective zones where audition is comfortable with tonal differences. At these levels audition can not only discern sounds, it can also recognize intervals and directions of variation, acting as a receiver whose frequency limits coincide with the selectivity limits. Outside these limits is a no-man's-land. Noise is detected, but without quality, without the possibility of distinction or analysis. In other words, the receiver seems to be provided with a diaphragm that closes at various levels and opens electively at others.

This opening and closing assuredly occur, and it can be easily conceived that any pathological disturbance may trouble the adaptive maneuver. But pathology is far from being the only cause.

In the beginning this selective auditory diaphragm is conditioned to listen to the environment. It is tuned to the voices that are willing to educate it, that show it the modulations within which language is structured. The adaptation of the diaphragm is essentially a function of the verbal flow that has to be absorbed by the auditory mouth.

The sonic and acoustic surrounding medium has the greatest possible influence. If the educating voice is harsh, there is the risk that the student will also develop a harsh voice simply because the receiver electively enjoys that verbal food. Clinical work confirms these facts every day. If the mother has a rough voice, in general her children will have similar voices.

But these factors are easily imagined, foreseen and measured. Other deeper and more troubling influences demonstrate once more the great fragility of the self-listening faculty, recent human acquisition that it is. These can be termed psychological factors, and they show the general applicability of the word "dissolution," so dear to Baillarger and Jackson. To listen and to listen to oneself are voluntary acts, recent achievements of evolution, while to hear is purely automatic. Listening is quickly replaced by hearing if any unfortunate experience occurs to break up the marvelous but unsteady functional structure.

Let an emotional shock take place, and the world of sound becomes painful and fatiguing. To hear, but no longer to listen, is a possible defense. The ear loses its adaptation and goes back to its primary function, that of defense, that which warns of danger, that which precedes the scolding and punishment considered unjustified. Many parents think that their authority is acknowledged when in fact their child's ear barely hears them and has not listened to them for a long time.

One's listening is easily disconnected, and only a considerable effort can restore it. It will soon be said that the child has no attention span, that his head is in the clouds, that he is not interested in his work, that he is asleep in his corner, or in other cases that he is turbulent, unbearable. Actually, he is hearing without listening.

Language is comparable to a pyramid built on shaky foundations. The apex projects into the infinite world of thought. Like an aerial, it can receive various beams and wavelengths. It can awaken in the machine beneath it translating mechanisms, which transmit verbal messages in semantic codes that are carefully chosen to convey to us, the primary interested party, a conscious and luminous image of that thought, which fills the limitless space of our pervasive unconscious.

Language allows us to establish a permanent contact with the immensity that pervades us. But even a minor pathological or psychological disturbance can destroy that wonderful order. We then become strangers to the supernatural world that we once

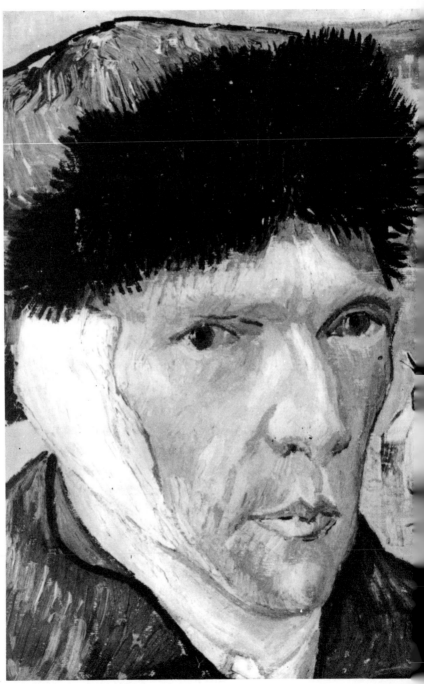

AN EASY WAY TO DISCONNECT ONE'S LISTENING...

felt and discovered through speech, and we forget the very principles of our verbal conditioning, as happens in cases of aphasia.
Would it be possible to reconstruct such a mechanism?

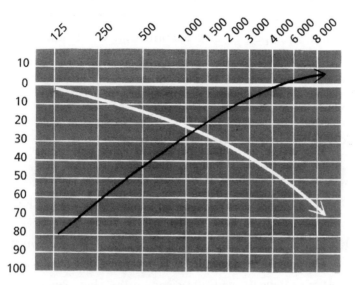

FIGURE 12. THE CONTOUR OF THE RESPONSE CURVE, WHICH MODELS ITSELF VERY
QUICKLY ON THE IMPOSED CURVE.

We sought answers about language by using the same techniques we had used to approach an understanding of the influences that condition singing. We needed to reconstruct the audi-
bility conditions of the initial period of language development and
to observe the consequences. During phonation we provided a
hyperaudition following a typical curve that delivered audition of
frequencies between 800 and 3,000 Hz. If the slope of this curve
is a minimum of 6 db per octave, the intelligibility of the language
used increases considerably and reaches its optimum. It is curious
to see how plastic the audition response curve is, how rapidly it
imitates and matches the imposed curve; however, we cannot
provide a well-founded physiological explanation of this effect.
The profile of the response curve quickly becomes identical with

that of the curve we have imposed as a control. Is it a question of adapting to the predetermined superimposition, or are we already witnessing a conditioning to the audition of the voice that has been strongly modified under the influence of the filters? Is there a mechanical reason of a physical or physiological nature? We are not equipped to give a correct answer to the problems raised by such a mechanism. What matters is that our goal has been attained.

■ Conditioning to Foreign Languages

The way we see it, everything connected with language comes back to the ear. Can anyone point out something that does not? Even in reading, which would seem to bring another kind of enrichment to language, every syllable, every word, every sentence has its reverberation, which refers to auditory memorization. You read, so to speak, with your ear on the alert. Remember that "ear" means the whole apparatus starting at the external auditory canal and ending at the corresponding cerebral zone. Everything passes through this network. Only with the deafmute does a detour awaken other conditioning (namely sight and proprioceptive sensations) that use the internal sensations to engender his emission, which education tries to make as close as possible to normal phonation.

In any case, there is no doubt that a foreign language is integrated by the ear. Nonetheless helped by text and image, the auditory acquisition is the essential, primordial acquisition. It is by hearing a language, and hearing it correctly, that it is learned.

What is meant by hearing or listening correctly?

Merely because one has difficulty learning a given foreign language does not mean one is deaf. One is merely electively deaf to that foreign language.

This notion is disconcerting at first but becomes obvious if we remember that the ear's conditioning to language is secondary and that its apprenticeship was in its habituation to the surrounding acoustic medium, which has determined the opening of the selective auditory diaphragm. This limitation, which is practically the rule, allowed us to master with desired finesse and agility only one sonic and rhythmic mode, which is peculiar to one language. But how different is the acoustic world of another language! A whole new conditioning has to be established. Without it all our attempts to articulate an emission are ineffective, knowing we cannot correctly control it. It concerns us henceforth to attempt to show that without conditioning to the new language, it would not be possible to approximate the fluent reproduction based in the complex notions of phonetics, even speech therapy. We are far from the simple and engaging way of acquiring language that originally allowed us to integrate our first language.

Our inhibition concerning any foreign language is increased by our unreasoning fear of ridicule. Our ear, that analytical receiver, turns into a mere aerial incapable of discerning, in the flood that overcomes it, the syllables that pile and mount up in a strange and troubling rhythm, hammering out intonations whose import we cannot quite grasp.

When it comes to foreign languages, we are as much at a loss as the aphasic is with all language.

To remedy this linguistic disarray we looked in the areas of audition and the audition-phonation circuit for a key that might explain this effect.

Where does conditioning to a foreign language begin?

If the language uses phonemes close to ours and in the same rhythm, it will certainly not take us long to reproduce all the sounds we are taught. But most foreign sounds are not likely to resemble ours. In some respect they are dissimilar. By the same techniques as before, using spectrum analysis displays or sound

THE DEVELOPMENT OF LANGUAGE WILL ALWAYS BE THE MOST FASCINATING HUM
GAME, NO MATTER HOW BADLY IT IS PLAYED.

spectrograms, we were gradually able to secure the envelope curves of the mean values of frequencies often encountered in the analysis of phrases collected from the same ethnic group. Thus, for example, the zone of greatest elected frequency concentration for French is found around 800 to 1,800 Hz, while for British English it extends between 2,000 and 12,000 Hz.

To perceive these frequency zones correctly, without the risk of introducing distortions through our auditory receiver, which operates as a filter, we have to adjust or, better still, condition ourselves to perceive in such a way that our optimal selectivity reaches that of the frequencies desired in our emission.

Again it is directly to language that we apply the new integrating techniques. The subject speaks, but as soon as he does, his audition is modified in such a way that all the sounds are made to pass through a selective channel that intentionally gives the desired quality of the language being studied.

The experiment can have spectacular results. A sentence in an unfamiliar language that is enunciated by the professor with the help of these techniques is reproduced almost from the beginning with amazing similarity. The most striking effect associated with the procedure is the feeling of liberation that is produced, and the disappearance of the inhibition that previously created negative sensations.

Large-scale experimental tests have confirmed the validity of these observations, and the techniques are now widely used in the teaching of foreign languages. Of course, the subject must also make an effort, and his contribution should not be minimized. His motivation remains incontestably a major factor, but his part is made much easier by removing inhibitions due to the incomprehensibility of the spoken tongue and to its consequent impossibility of reproduction.

The conditioning to which we submit the ear during foreign language training may be of two kinds:

- The subject, provided with a headset connected to a unit ensuring correct audition, repeats the instructor's words, or
- He controls the process himself by using a tape that inputs the phonic elements directly into the machine as needed.

Here we glimpse one of the key elements in audio-visual techniques. More and more use is being made of these techniques, which offer the student not only the teacher's basic course, but also examples of fluent language of which he can immediately make practical use. Left to himself in front of the machine, he has an image before him, and the corresponding text is read into his ear by a tape recorder and a headset. This technique offers clear advantages. The individualization of the process contributes greatly to its success. The subject makes use of his machine according to his own inclination in a progression that allows for independent repetition at will. He is not subjected to critical attention from the teacher, and that freedom is a significant factor in achieving progress right from the start. An easy, agreeable, and amusing game of voluntary repetition is established. The development of language will always be the most fascinating human game, no matter how badly it is played. It is unique to man and is his most complete, farthest advanced, and best used humanization factor. But the fragility experienced by infants while they construct their audio-vocal circuit is even greater in adults.

The increased fragility is due to the adult's greater inhibitions; his social position hampers him, and his fear of ridicule detracts from his enjoyment of this game of linguistic construction. The habit of constantly calling upon his intelligence to understand things is of no assistance to him; on the contrary, his intelligence interferes with the circuit, the track that has to be laid down; instead of helping, it gets in the way. What matters at the beginning, you will recall, is the installation of the network, progressively setting up its lines and designing its diagrams of verbal flow; then, if nothing upsets the person, semantic crystallization will rapidly take place.

It serves no purpose to try to understand everything from the beginning. That is not where you started when you first learned your mother tongue. Undoubtedly haste creates confusion at this stage, and in any case, what is the point of hurrying? Our system, accustomed from infancy to use its first network, no longer needs as much time to work out a second one. The adult's maturity will allow him to speed up the process to some extent, skimming over certain stages; but these stages still have to be traversed in any case.

Though audio-visual techniques may seem ideal at the start, they conceal the serious risk that auditory sensitivity differs for each individual.

Knowing whether the subject makes a mental image out of his visual image that is somewhat different from the one his neighbor makes does not really matter. The synthetic structure of vision will give each of them an almost identical overall value in the end. By contrast, we do not know how the essential instrument of audio-phonation (namely our auditory receiver) functions in performing an analysis. The whole process of regulation depends on the voluntary acquisition of articulation movements, which requires that the subject have normal automatic movements. Language is not made. It consists entirely of highly elaborate, secondarily organized movements, which are only inherent to man insofar as he is invested in his human character.

If the auditory receiver is defective, or even just frozen in a single position, and is incapable of unconscious kinesthetic modification, all the practical techniques we employ will be useless. The recordings, whatever they may be, will perish like many others at the back of a drawer, waiting under the dust for some new passing fancy.

In such cases the method is less to blame than the factors

involved in auditory integration. Forcing people to understand things in a different way requires them to listen in a different way and thus demands that they vary their mode of control and start again the initial process of auditory integration of the new rhythms and sounds. The astonishing results produced by these audio-vocal techniques occur because they electronically create for our absorption the acoustic medium needed to establish auto-control. That which remains, phonation, follows next.

To speak French, then, is to hear and listen in French; to speak English is to hear and listen in English. To speak bad English, for a Frenchman, is to hear English and listen to it with French ears.

It is imperative to use high quality equipment in language laboratories. A defective element in the setup of the verbal system can compromise the proper transmission of the message that is to be absorbed; moreover, any alterations along the way that completely modify the original course of the message make its processing that much more difficult. Imperfections may be found in any element of the system. Thus the recording has to be of excellent quality; the spaces left for repetition, called sonic blanks, must be judiciously distributed; the recorders must reproduce with fidelity, without any distortion, what is on the tape.

The required linearity — for example up to 12,000 Hz for English — is absolutely necessary. We have seen whole laboratories standing empty, because the students had become discouraged and refused to continue working with banks of tape recorders whose curves, all different from one another, introduced distortions and made the original acoustic signal unrecognizable. If the listening ear has to correct or use much effort catching what has been said, the desired goal cannot be attained. The proliferation of poor quality tape recorders has been counter productive. Bearing in mind the plasticity of an auditory curve, which can model itself on the imposed curve, a machine whose curve is truncated at 3,000 or 4,000 Hz can produce auditory conditioning that is the opposite of what is desired. We have even come across tape recorders that were intended to educate the ear, but which would cause everything to break down around 500 or even 300 Hz. The currently admitted standards that allow a drop after 5,000 Hz are only defensible from a commercial standpoint and are dangerous and ineffective.

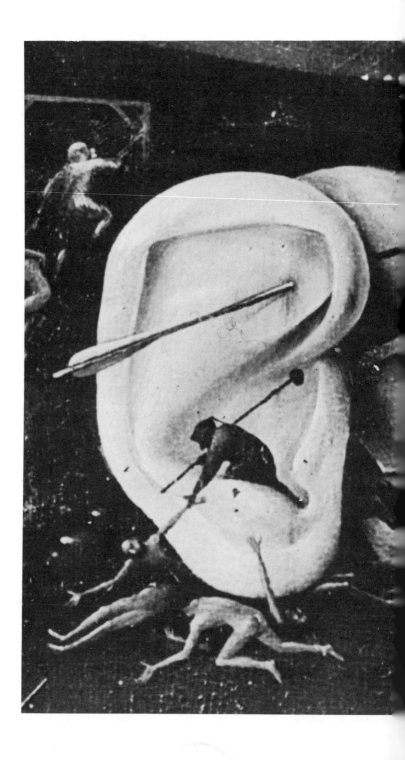

The Leading Ear

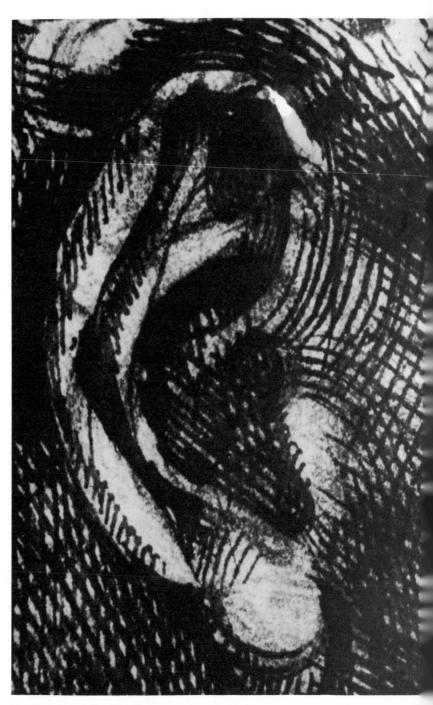

DRAWING OF THE EAR BY MICHELANGELO.

*"And the good ear will
listen to wisdom."*
ECCL. III, 29

■ The Leading Ear

Open your ear, and be sure it is the right one, because everything we have presented so far apparently only goes in one of your two ears. Here is an additional complication that really seems to go against nature.

We will not go so far as to ask ourselves what Paul Raugé asked with great emphasis in *Annales internationales de laryngologie, d'otologie et de rhinologie* (July – August 1896): "Why do we have two ears when one would be sufficient, and what is the reason for this multiplicity of organs? This abundance runs counter to nature's customary frugality." We shall not ask such a question, because we would be running the risk of angering nature, which is so prolific, so rich, so generous; and in truth not dealing with it would only be sidestepping the problem.

Earlier we surmised that the ear was an organ initially provided to hear and locate noises. Two ears then appear indispensable to identify, by intersection of their fields of perception, the position of sound sources. So acoustical detection is enough to justify having one ear on each side of our head. However, during past millennia functional modifications have become crystallized in man himself and in his whole structure. Thus, as will be recalled, our acoustic antenna has literally parted company with its first activity.

Why should one ear be "the good one," to use the proverbial expression? Our present knowledge fails to provide us with an adequate answer to this question. We will allow ourselves to advance some ideas to explain the phenomenon, knowing full well that thereby we expose ourselves to criticism. Surely it is only human to go beyond admitted or accepted facts in seeking a cause — at least as human as to take aggressive action, a more common attitude because it is easier.

However, before entering the domain of hypothesis, let us proceed with our experimentation.

■ The Leading Ear and Singing

While we interfered with the singer's hearing in order to determine the parallel between displacements of the auditory scotoma and the vocal scotoma, we discovered that response reactions obtained from the ears were not identical.

Since then we have systematically examined this fact — whose discovery took place around 1950 — by using two setups, both of which are very simple and can easily be copied by any researcher.

1. The first setup includes a microphone that feeds the singer's voice into a linear amplifier, the output of which is connected to two parallel earphones. An attenuator allows the subject to hear himself either through both ears, or through one or the other, by changing the "balance" level. This experiment is, of course, recorded.

We restricted our experimentation at the outset to experienced professionals — famous singers for the most part. One was chosen because he had a technique that to our knowledge has never been criticized even by his colleagues, which is so remarkable that it deserves to be stressed. Furthermore, he was extraordinarily resistant to fatigue. Our subject submitted willingly to the experiment. Our interest in him increased because the previous night he had finished a series of 400 performances of the same work, and every night he had done one or two encores of the same aria he was to sing during the experiment. Choosing him showed our desire to use a case where the singing was especially well produced, solidly based, and supported by established habits. Our observations follow:

- Listening with both ears, with the earphones being balanced, the voice was the same as was obtained from this singer without any apparatus. According to him, there seemed to be no change.
- Suppressing left ear input, leaving the right ear alone in its controlling position, repetition of the experiment showed apparently only slight modifications. To a very sensitive ear the sounds seemed lighter, more ethereal, more modulated, more precise, more distinct, of a more perfect legato. The singer mentioned that he was aware of his greater fluency.
- On the other hand, when we reversed our control system and placed it on the left ear, eliminating the right, not only did the exceptional fluency vanish, but all the professional qualities acquired by the singer broke down. We witnessed a true dissolution of all the skill so ably controlled a few moments before. The voice became heavy, coarse, less colorful, and off pitch; and, worst of all, the rhythm slowed down considerably. Thus, twenty years of brilliantly performed singing, and the thousand repetitions of the same aria, left no trace after the simple elimination of one ear by its removal from the circuit.

2. In the second experiment we used saturation in first one ear and then the other. Again, we found that eliminating only one of the two ears yielded the same experimental results, namely altered of vocal quality, disappearance of pitch, and slowed rhythm.

This last effect, which is the most remarkable to the ear of an experimenter not trained in singing techniques, may go so far as to double the time normally required for the performance of a musical phrase. This destruction of the rhythm is beyond the reach of the singer's will; the subject becomes aware of it if someone beats time for him, but he is incapable of following the tempo. There he stands, inhibited, full of ineffective good will, troubled and confused by his inability to keep to the correct

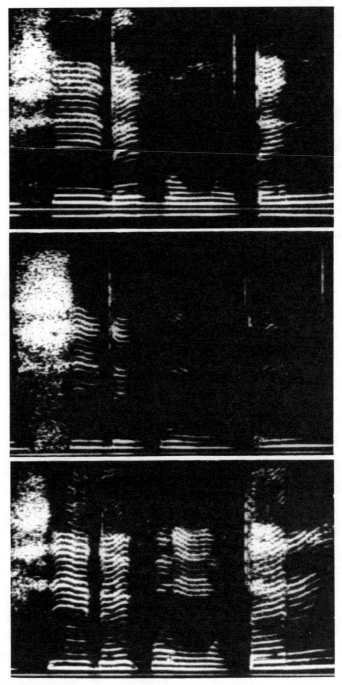

FIGURE 13.
A. SONOGRAM: WHEN HEARD WITH BOTH EARS.
B. SONOGRAM: WHEN THE RIGHT EAR IS SUPPRESSED.
C. SONOGRAM: WHEN THE LEFT EAR IS SUPPRESSED.

rhythm. The blockage is not even limited to singing. During the whole experiment the subject becomes slow, moves like a robot, and seems to lose his capacity for carrying out voluntary acts. This reveals one of the most extraordinary characteristics of the structuring of those acquired acts which involve the will.

The conclusions we have drawn since 1952 from this important experimental fact made us think that there is a preferential ear, designated to execute the more special and more precise control functions, and endowed with an acquired functional dominance in which the power of the will plays a part. We thus decided to name it the *leading ear*. Current usage denotes the leading eye as the one that aims. This analogy seemed justified; and from that perspective, the singer is a technician whose mastery of auditory control compares to that of the marksman in the visual plane; the singer in some way *aims* at the sounds he emits.

■ The Leading Ear and the Spoken Voice

Since that time we have worked unceasingly on the problem of auditory dominance. We easily transfered this experimentation, which is simple to carry out and was very familiar to us from our work with singers, to the domain of spoken language. This logical move now seems the obvious next step, and yet it took us a long time to make — a full year. It is strange how the thought mechanisms that incite and steer research are sometimes slow to start, but with hindsight it is easy to build up similar constructs.

However that may be, it happened one day that an actor submitted to the experiments described above. The results far surpassed our expectations.

When he listened with both ears using the normal amplifier, nothing happened. When the left ear was suppressed, the voice became lighter, with more timbre, and higher-pitched. This fact was the more remarkable because our actor had a very low-pitched voice. By contrast, when the right ear was eliminated, the result was complete ruin. Our actor was left with a flat voice,

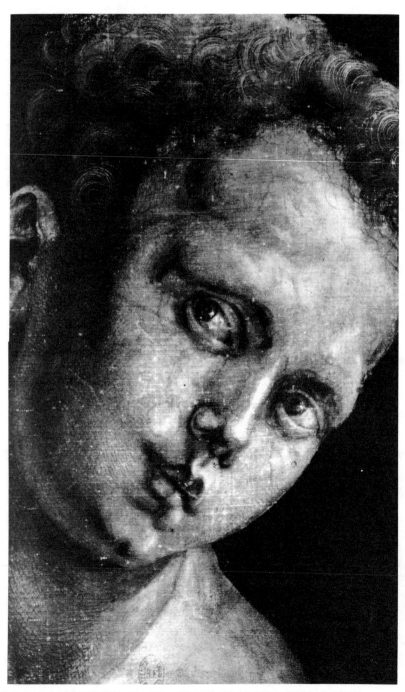

THE WHOLE ORGANIZATION OF LANGUAGE DEPENDS ON THE AUDITORY RECEIVER.

without tone or timbre and badly produced; it soon became filled with hesitations, with the "ah's" more and more prolonged. At the end of a few sentences this mumbling became interspersed with double syllables and interrupted by blockage, ending to our amazement in typical stuttering.

The result we had obtained seemed so important that we repeated our experiments with the same subject several times, and we finally had to conclude that these facts were accurate.

What an adventure! We never suspected that this simple experimental finding would engage our laboratory activities and hold our attention for more than ten years.

Immediately we hopefully drew two logical conclusions:

- One of the ears is chosen as the preferential one for regulating the spoken voice.
- We should consider the possibility of research for an etiology of stuttering in the disturbance of the leading ear regulation.

By experimental process, using numerous laboratory tests, we verified the first hypothesis with great success. Since then, our research in auditory dominance has largely passed the stage of the pure experiment to become an integral and essential part of our clinical testing. With a self-assured, solidly based voice, firm in its timbre and rhythm, the suppression of one or the other ear produces as a rule the following results:

- The voice, listening with both ears free, becomes disturbed as soon as the controlling ear, which does the auditory aiming, is affected. The voice becomes deeper and at the same time loses timbre. Only a few exceptions to this result are possible.
- Rhythm problems are more variable and virtually specific to each individual. Stuttering, which was produced in our remarkable early experiment, is not always found. Rhythm always undergoes modification, which is characterized by a lengthened verbal flow associated with marked irregularities and breaks.

The aim of our research was to discover what factors determined the leading ear in subjects who had good singing voices. It soon became apparent that voices without richness or assurance, which were emitted with difficulty, often corresponded to badly conditioned or underdeveloped auditory controls.

The leading ear was proving to be of considerable importance in language troubles, particularly since any awareness we could bring about on such a dominance could conceivably reopen many seemingly dead-end cases. If it did not exist, would that mean that the aiming of sounds was impossible? Might it not be the explanation for an absence of lateral fixation? What was its ruling function in the field of attention? Could it play a part in memory? Might its inefficiency or insufficiency in the aiming of external listening be causing, in short, the poor conditioning of auto-control and of auto-information?

We knew that each hypothesis could not be substantiated overnight, but if it was proved to be correct it would have immense theoretical consequences. We started little by little to work out a series of tests and countertests, which at first allowed us to state the following:

- Establishing auto-control by a single ear in a voice that is either disorganized or not yet organized always produces an improvement, no matter which ear is chosen. In effect, the moment one ear is eliminated from the circuit by any means one decides to use, the voice and the spoken sequence become controlled. It appears that cybernetically the coexistence of two auditory receivers can be, at the very least, a troublesome factor.
- Evaluating the yield of each of the two receivers determines auditory dominance. However, it must be admitted that it is not always easy to get the evidence because:

1. Either the ear of the experimenter/clinician is not sufficiently practiced or is deficient, or
2. In the course of the test no noticeable difference is found.

In the first case, where the clinician has insufficient auditory competence but often has to diagnose very subtle variations of quality or vocal rhythm, laboratory examinations may actually help his search. In the majority of cases a test controlled by spectrum analysis or sound spectrogram usually shows differences that are sufficient to determine the leading ear.

In the second case we can only say that the leading ear has not yet reached sufficient maturity to become differentiated. No examination can be of any help, and neither the hearing of the clinician, no matter how practiced, nor visual observations are likely to support a possible orientation.

This determination is clinically interesting since the whole organization of language depends on the auditory receiver. We have since developed and will talk later about techniques that allow us to educate hearing until the leading ear makes its appearance.

■ The Leading Ear and Stuttering

It is tempting to imagine that a problem in the regulation of the audio vocal system can result in stuttering. Some people persist in refusing to face this fact even though they have no contrary evidence on which to base their opinion. Meanwhile, everything points to poor control. But the circumstances that determine it are not always identical, and we firmly believe that the differences of opinion occur because these circumstances are often difficult to analyze.

We agree that we were undoubtedly in a hurry in mechanizing the audition-phonation system. We were undoubtedly very quick to say that the loss of the leading ear is the determining factor in the loss of rhythm control. We were tempted to believe in these relationships all the more because all the stutterers we examined at the beginning were affected by a slight leading side deficiency. Furthermore, we were comfortable in our conviction based on the successful treatments obtained through education of the leading ear. That seemed enough to convince any skeptic. Yet in truth the problem is not nearly as simple as we originally imagined. Difficulties and setbacks made us reexamine it.

Let us look first at the facts established by experimental process, which gives some certainty as we proceed with our explanations.

- First of all, the disturbance of the leading ear in a subject having normal phonation may bring about stuttering. But this result is not found in all subjects. It is in fact somewhat rare.
- In support of our hypothesis is a test of "delayed feedback," which was brought to light by John Lee and used for a long time by John Black of the University of Columbus in Ohio. Delayed feedback refers to the delay that is reflected in the feedback due to control of the input into the receiver. We already came across these concepts in the earlier description of the few elements of cybernetics.

How is the feedback increased? In 1949 John Lee and John Black used the following experimental setup: the subject speaks into a microphone that receives the voice, and the same is recorded by a recording head on a magnetic wire or tape; further on, a mobile playback head allows controlled increase, along a metal strip, of the distance that separates the recording head from the playback head. From this distance and from the speed at which the tape unrolls, it is possible to deduce the time introduced in the delayed playback when the subject, as he speaks, rehears his voice through earphones. The result is dephasing of regulation that invariably results in stuttering when the feedback delay reaches a value of 0.15 second.

According to some people, this artificial stuttering does not deserve to be classed with real stuttering. Subtle differences and divergent views can be explained according to different interpretations of the same mechanism that is instrumental in producing speech. In any case, whatever name one may want to give it, that a regulation problem exists cannot be denied without contradicting the most elementary evidence. We agree that it is sufficient to know or determine the rung on which our feedback rests.

That may be anywhere along the ladder, from the receiver to the cortex. For the reader who may have joined us along the way, we must insist that according to our terminology, the ear begins at the pinna and extends far along the cerebral cortex. The feedback thus has to traverse highly differentiated zones and is thereby subjected to a thousand and one orders and restraints.

But if audition is unarguably one of the most determinant sensory elements in our verbal flow control, it is not the only one, as we believed at the start. Thus, in order to advance further into the etiological research on speech, we resumed our laboratory experiments with the courage born of setbacks. Our purpose was either to uncover the main lines that would allow us to detect a regulating element that would affect the ear in some other way or to find other non-auditory feedbacks susceptible to disturbances.

We had noticed that our failures involved mostly stutterers who could not speak correctly aloud, even when they were alone, that is, under conditions such that no outside factor could intervene as a causal agent. It is known that when they are alone, stutterers are able to speak with facility, even with eloquence. It is also known that they can easily recite a memorized text, and the number of well-known actors who have had this handicap is beyond count. By contrast, our recalcitrant stutterers were incapable of reciting a text they knew perfectly. We then decided to isolate certain subjects taken from each group and have them talk aloud in a room, in which unbeknownst to them we had placed a listening apparatus. Thanks to this subterfuge we could record and analyze their voices, while at the same time we could listen at leisure directly to the disturbances that were manifested when, say, a noise occurred behind a door or a third party entered the room.

What is remarkable is that the stutterer who resists all correction always stays more or less the same. His voice does not undergo any change for the better, no matter what environmental conditions one tries to create for him. By contrast, the second type, the sort with whom our efforts always bear fruit, clearly shows two very different and characteristic ways of behaving. If he is isolated, he behaves exactly like anyone else. He uses a frank, self-assured, often harmonious voice; his words follow his thought flow admirably, and he intimately adheres to them. But this whole marvelous activation comes crashing down as soon as the charm of isolation is broken. The rhythm no longer has anything in common with that which characterized the initial flow — an essential fact that is very noticeable in the analysis of recordings. The voice's tone is modified: it becomes monotonous, without color, without timbre.

In other words, the stutterer of this type seems to fall between two poles: at the one extreme the non-stutterer, who speaks correctly no matter what the circumstances, and at the other, the uncontrollable stutterer, who cannot say anything regardless of the conditions in which he is placed. To the observer it appears that these two types have only one way of communicating information; one represents consistent control of this way while the other represents consistent failure of control. Our stutterer who stands between these two groups benefits paradoxically by two ways of communication. When he is alone, he talks like anybody else; by contrast, in public he is as deprived of oral language as the one who is permanently affected by his stuttering.

We could deduce from this that our stutterer belongs to a category of individuals endowed with two control modes, one normal and the other disturbed.

Let us try to analyze what may be happening when our isolated stutterer starts to talk normally. We can easily imagine this test without necessarily being stutterers. What happens to us if we talk to ourselves out loud, for example in our office? Our self-information is obvious; we are not crazy enough to address our sentences to our furniture, our walls, our ceiling. Even in thought we do not address a speech to a chair or a chandelier, even a lighted chandelier. We talk to ourselves; we inform ourselves. If we record our voice, analysis reveals the characteristics we find under many other circumstances. Only an attitude of defense, of aggression, of anguish, can noticeably modify these characteristics. The timbre changes, and even the rhythm is altered. It is more common to mumble before a large audience than before one or two people, especially for someone who is not used to public speaking. Is this what the stutterer feels, this second manner of defective control, which systematically appears in him, but which for us only comes into play in unfavorable circumstances? Aside from more or less extensive rhythm troubles, recordings made during these disturbances reveal a very noticeable modification in voice timbre. It is an unusual voice that comes out, without body, we might say if we did not know otherwise.

The ear is certainly the primary receiver during phonation. It exerts its regulation on all the parameters: intensity, volume, duration. One, however, seems to partly escape it, that of flow control. By *flow* in verbal emission we mean the acoustic stream that comes out of our mouth in successive waves, shaped in its form and volume by our articulation and poured over us like the filling out of a cream puff, as I often describe it to children in treatment.

Is this just a mental image? Can we imagine that sound really flows out of us, like a liquid? A simple experiment can demonstrate the truth of this assertion. If you isolate the body, for example by putting your head in a baffle, you immediately disturb the whole regulation. The voice changes, loses its warmth and its low frequencies, and becomes shrill; the rhythm accelerates and becomes abrupt and inexact; conversation is hard to sustain.

Even more striking is the result obtained with stutterers when they are first initiated to bodily self-information. Only a few are unaffected by this test. Language immediately becomes what it was during isolation of the subject.

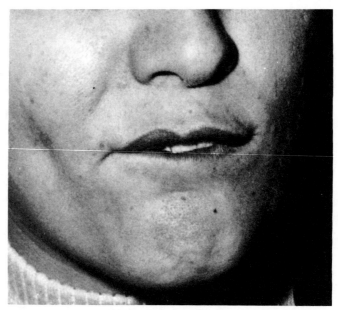

ASIDE FROM MORE OR LESS EXTENSIVE RHYTHM TROUBLES...

We tried to apply this procedure in all cases of treatment involving stutterers. Only a few stutterers who were blocked even in isolation were unresponsive to this method of education. We wondered whether they might be lacking a certain ability to respond to the acoustic flow over the body. We thus tried to discover the cutaneous zones that were sensitive to variations of sound-generating pressure. The results were true "cutaneous audiograms," which we named "dermagrams."

The skin is sensitive to acoustic pressures of 10 to 15 decibels applied with a vibrator. Responses to these stimuli vary according to the location explored: the hand and the fingers, especially the palmar face of the last phalanx of the index, are more sensitive than the skin of the elbow, for example. A long-range statistical study will ultimately allow us to determine the elective area to be detected.

Our first investigations into this field allow us to state that cutaneous sensitivity and the quality of phonation control are in direct

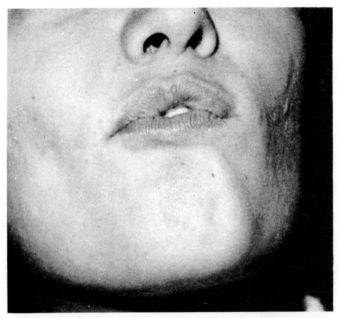

...IT IS AN UNUSUAL VOICE THAT COMES WITHOUT BODY.

proportion. More precise control is associated with more accurate rhythm and greater skin sensitivity. The more persistent stutterers are practically deprived of the dermal control mechanism: 80 or even 100 db are sometimes necessary to awaken their sensation of acoustic pressures. Thus rolling of speech along their bodies turns out to be at least uncontrolled, if not impossible.

When such difficulties appear, the initiation of the body into language cannot be achieved through speech. In such cases the subject does not utilize his body to register speech. This led us to the idea of exposing the subject to education via an electronic setup, which allowed auto-control by ear, while at the same time the whole body was immersed in a sound bath. The essential purpose was to make the stutterer sense verbal flow over the skin.

The subject thus learns to use his body like a musical instrument. To speak is to play one's own body.

Laterality

WHAT IS LATERALITY?

The right hand of the Lord doeth valiantly.
The right hand of the Lord is exalted:
the right hand of the Lord doeth valiantly.

PSALM 118, 15-16

■ Laterality

To speak of a leading ear is to admit that one ear plays a dominant role. Surely we cannot proceed without looking for the reason for this differentiation. For years we limited ourselves to experimental results and refused to venture beyond statements of fact; we knew too well how much trouble we could bring on ourselves by indulging in speculation. Eventually curiosity broke down our resistance. Having gone from the ear to language, and then to the leading ear, we are about to lead the reader toward another magnetic pole, that of laterality.

What is laterality? Nothing is simpler and nothing is more obscure. By laterality we mean the fact of being right-handed or left-handed.

Where does laterality come from? In the present state of our knowledge we must say that God only knows. This statement may be unscientific but it is nonetheless very satisfying.

There has to be a beginning. Laterality could not have appeared spontaneously without any intervening factor, and the fact that its origin has not yet been discovered does not exclude the existence of a cause and its consequent appearance.

Contemplating a right and a left is to make a curious differentiation for an essentially bilateral animal. In effect, with the exception of his innards, man is symmetrical, like the great majority of living beings. Why the devil did we one day decide to give one of our sides a functional advantage? What is most remarkable is that this specialization seems to be peculiar to man. Animals have no laterality to speak of. A few actions acquired by habit are performed after training by one or the other limb, without any spontaneous motivation having started them by preference to use one side or the other.

Man seems to have been lateralized since earliest times. Moreover, wherever in the world man has arisen, as a rule his laterality has been right-dominant. No nations or culture of left-handed humans exist on this globe, and no pictorial or graphic sign in diverse civilizations ever showed they were executed by any but right-handers.

That man is right-handed seems to have been admitted as a normal fact from earliest antiquity. The left-hander contradicts this rule, and the anomaly is sufficient to be taken as a distinguishing sign of the individual in question. To be left-handed is to be unlike everybody else. One may recall the battle described in Judges (XX, 16) where seven hundred left-handed warriors are called upon to disconcert the enemy. Man is always surprised when faced with this backward counter-attack of the left hander.

From all the evidence, right-hand dominance is statistically overwhelming. However, attempts to explain the phenomenon usually serve only to create more confusion. Endless and extravagant hypotheses have been put forward, but none has contributed any truly decisive or determinant elements. If we only wanted to produce a simple history of right-handedness, we would worry very little about the origins of this human acquisition. But we are strongly convinced that it is one of the keys of man's humanization and that without it there is no language.

A few facts make us lean toward this opinion. Let us cite some examples:

- Laterality constantly fails to appear where language fails to be acquired. Alvez Garcia, in his *Les Troubles du Langage* reports by way of proof a very ample and detailed study of the manual ambivalence in writing encountered in deafmutes. He can advance the statistical figure, astonishing at first sight, of 100% ambidexterity in writing for deafmutes. Our investigations in this field fully confirm these results.
- Even without looking to the extreme case of deafmutes, we are able to state that failure to acquire verbal language corresponds in large part to underdeveloped, unstructured laterality.
- Abnormal and debilitated persons are generally poorly lateralized. This dyslaterality has already been noted by Lannelongue.

It would seem that laterality and language go hand in hand. Which presides at the birth of the other? In the face of such profound and complex phenomena, it is always foolhardy to give an opinion as to the mutual influence of two such complex mechanisms, namely whether laterality helped to shape language or whether language is at the origin of laterality.

It is most probable that neither of these mechanisms can exist without the other, and we hope it is not too much of a contradiction to say that one generates the other and vice versa. A curious law of genetics is that two functions are in fact one and the same thing when their parallel evolution most likely constitutes only one gradual speciation, which is the result of their interrelationship.

During language education we observe a crystallization of laterality as language is elaborated.

Deeply ingrained reactions do of course exist whose counter-reactions establish a permanent bond between their different structures, but they certainly do not occur one without the other. We have proof of this; when we suppress the hearing of the leading ear, we observe a dissolution of the spoken language accompanied by rhythm troubles and a spatial disorganization of language. In fact, are we not acting on laterality, and is not language merely a response to the secondary organization constituted by lateralization? And can we not admit that laterality is built through progressive acquisition of the design of language — and through language itself?

■ Auditory Laterality and Bodily Laterality

It is inconceivable to deal with the subject of auditory laterality without including it in the problem of body laterality in general. A historical overview of the study of lateralization fits naturally at this point, all the more since it was the study of language that led the first researchers to note that a bodily dominance was selectively fixed on half of the body. To have a leading ear is to have at one's command a functionally dominant ear. The leading ear attributes to this perceptual organ a special human adaptation which requires more specific physical qualities for its functioning and which bears witness to a recent, new acquisition in the overall human scale.

Our nerve bundles, which gather sensory impressions, are a network of crossed paths; it is the same for those nerves that transmit motor impulses to our muscles. Thus the whole sensitivity of the right side of the body is centralized toward the left half of the brain, while the left side of the body projects onto the right half of the brain. Motor activity is similarly determined by nervous impulses that start from the left half of the brain for the right side of the body and from the right half of the brain for the left side of the body. While some direct bundles do exist, they are of much smaller functional importance.

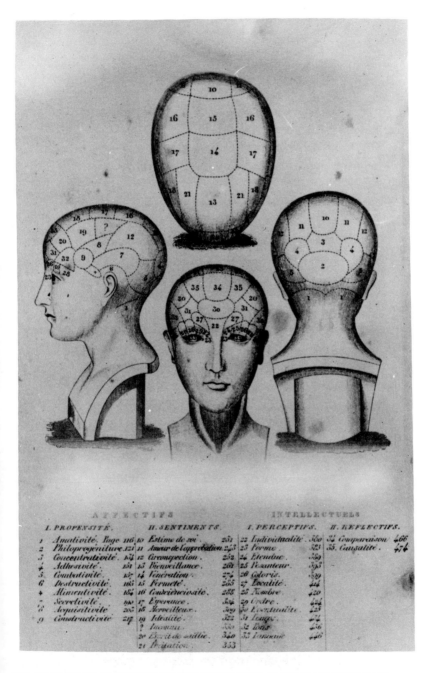

THE GREAT NAMES OF MEDICINE DEBATED WHICH PARTS OF THE BRAIN CONTROLLED WHICH FACULTIES.

If there is a dominant side (usually the right), the left half of the brain assumes a special role. It is essentially a question of role, because [at the time this is written] nothing so far distinguishes one cerebral hemisphere from the other. They are identically symmetrical.

This notion of cerebral dominance was upheld in the past by Broca, a surgeon of great skill. In the second half of the 19th century he used anatomical observation to establish the two following essential facts: that a language center exists in the brain and that it is located in the left half of the brain.

Judging from reactions of specialists of the time, Broca must have had immense daring even to mention his clinical observations. It is difficult for us now, from our historical perspective, to imagine the violence of the storm that broke when this new idea was unleashed on the conceptions of that time.

Broca was the first to dare to put a functional label on a cerebral convolution; more than that, he spotted on that convolution what he believed to be a specific zone that was responsible for language. Others, particularly Pierre Marie, later insisted that Broca's observation, which broke like a thunderclap over the session of April 18, 1861 of the Société d'Anthropologie, was not as well founded as its author had thought. Still others such as Trousseau believed that the overall disintegrations of memorization that accompanied the lesions that Broca used as evidence were purely mechanical elements. Nevertheless, the young surgeon from Bicêrte remains the great promoter of the study of language; he opened a new era, which we could call the neurological era of language. Broca went even further; in April 1863, with highly scientific restraint, he was able to point to the left-hand dominance of cerebral lesions affecting language. Aside from a few murmurs from Gustave Dax, who claimed that his father Marc Dax had located this faculty in the left hemisphere, Broca is recognized as the one who with extraordinary clarity and as yet unrefuted foresight brought to light cerebral laterality. In 1865 in a report to the Academy of Medicine he defined his thinking on cerebral dominance, and the lines he wrote on that occasion retain a striking relevancy today.

Without retracing the whole history, the greatest names in medicine were locked in endless battle over which part of the brain controlled which faculty. Barely fifty years had elapsed since Gall's phrenology conceived of localizing animal and human aptitudes in various cerebral regions. His report, entitled *Research on the Nervous System in General and the Brain in particular,* presented (with Spurzheim) at the Institut de France in 1808 defined a general outline. The attacks on his theory were so violent that even his great supporters, such as Bouillaud, could not keep him, as he deserved, in the ranks of the true innovators. Nothing survived of his thought but the legendary "mathematician's bump." This malicious relic of a somewhat daring extrapolation hazarded by Gall affirmed that the content (in this case, the brain) had to act on the container (the skull), so that on a simple morphological aspect of the cranium, Gall presumed to be able to determine the aptitudes from various contours.

Broca did render homage to Gall and recognized in him the seeker, the forerunner of localization, and a fine anatomist. It is easy to understand why Gall was not able, by his own unsupported efforts in 1808, to find everything. Even now, a century and a half later, we are far from knowing everything.

Following Broca, many of the greatest names in medicine took an interest in the problems of language. Trousseau, Fleury, Ogle, Finkelnburg, Wernicke, Kussmaul, Charcot, Dejerine, Pierre Marie, Foix, Moutier, each by precise clinical and anatomical studies cast some light on this enormously complex problem. The complexity, truly did not seem to unduly trouble our pioneers.

From Broca's viewpoint a center of language existed; it was situated at the left side of the brain, below the inferior frontal gyrus. Any lesion electively striking this zone brought about the loss of speech and constituted a clinical entity that he designated "aphemia." He saw in this center the locus of the coordination necessary for the development of speech.

In short, Broca's viewpoint was somewhat mechanistic. Many followed in his footsteps, while others like Trousseau saw in speech disabilities only an impairment of intelligence and a deterioration of word verbal memory. Amnesia was the dominant character of the disease that Broca tried to describe. Trousseau in 1864 substituted the term "aphasia" for aphemia, which he found improper, and made of it a memory disease, an amnesia of the spoken act. He was to be followed along this path by other clinicians, such as Fleury and Ogle who went beyond him with their theories and who, with Finkelnburg in 1870, reached the conclusion that the maladies described by Broca were in fact only impairments affecting conceptual formation. The term "asymbolia" was introduced to denote the condition.

Elsewhere the mechanistic viewpoint was living through a more splendid epic. In 1869 Charleston Bastian, a London physician associated with National Hospital, promoted a more extensive and detailed mapping than Broca had proposed. With a clinical sense backed by an extraordinary analytical spirit, he detected four different clinical aspects of disease where speech was concerned: one located in Broca's center and causing the condition described by Broca as *aphemia*; a second affecting a zone situated higher up on the third frontal gyrus and causing a loss of writing ability or *agraphia*; a third responding to a breakdown of the relays operating the connection of verbal auditory memorization and causing *aphasia*; and finally, a fourth that became established when a lesion chose to afflict the auditory verbal center where our acoustic memories are stored and caused *amnesia*.

Bastian opened the way for the associationists. From then on it was a race to see who would find the best explanation by means of intercerebral circuits and relays going from one center to another. Wernicke and Kussmaul were the first participants and were followed by others. In fact, everyone seemed to be right, since the tableau of language difficulties covers such a wide clinical range that it is impossible to assign a strict and specific label to each description.

A historical overview of aphasia stresses that two movements were created and confronted each other. For the one, association and localization remain absolute and verifiable; the others, by contrast, reject the first group and go so far as to deny localization and association altogether. Many attempts at conciliation, the last to date being that of Foix and his students, failed in spite of laudable efforts to bring the two schools together into a more general and eclectic viewpoint.

In this intensely heated debate, while Broca and Trousseau passionately defended their respective positions, a conciliatory voice was raised but not heard. Yet the wisdom of its arguments was astonishing, perhaps too astonishing for those arguments to be understood. In any case, Baillarger, their promoter, spoke into a void, and his address to the Academy of Medicine in 1865, one of the most remarkable ever made on the construction of language, had no impact. Fortunately an English physician, Hughlings Jackson, exploited with incomparable genius what he called the Baillarger principle. For twenty years he collected clinical observations in support of Baillarger's position. He drew from them conclusions whose importance is only now being assessed, but he had no more luck than Baillarger himself and could not get anybody to listen to him. It was not until 1913 that the name of Jackson was evoked by Pick, and it is above all Henry Head who deserves credit for forcefully introducing Jackson's ideas, described in 1885, by publishing them in 1915 in *Brain*.

What was it that Baillarger said that was so extraordinary? We must refer to Jackson for the answer. He stated Baillanger's principle in the clearest possible terms: "Disorders of the nervous system have to be considered as reversals of evolution, that is, as dissolutions."

In other words, if we apply this principle to the study of the shaping of a human act as we conceive it, an act differentiated from one executed by an animal, we acknowledge an evolutionary progression that takes us through the following steps:

- From automatism toward the voluntary act,
- From the simple toward the complex, and
- From the rigidly organized toward the more flexible

Thus, the human scaffolding appears to be a second acquisition built upon an ancient structure, certainly more solid and more deeply anchored than the new building on top. The latter seems no doubt prodigious, but it is more fragile and is ready to collapse like a house of cards.

Following this principle, language dissolutions appear in a new light, and from there the study of the different stages in the return to an earlier state — a regression of sorts — makes it easier to understand the many forms such a pathology may assume, as Henry Head remarked in 1920.

Head likewise studied the problems that this regression brought forth into the domain of sensory perception: spatial localization of sensation is destroyed, while discrimination of degrees of intensity becomes impaired.

The outstanding salient fact from the preceding discussion is that dissolution always impairs organization. Does not laterality also correspond, more than any other acquisition, to a late organization? Has it not reached a degree of perfection that makes our most automatic acts become the most faithful executors of our will?

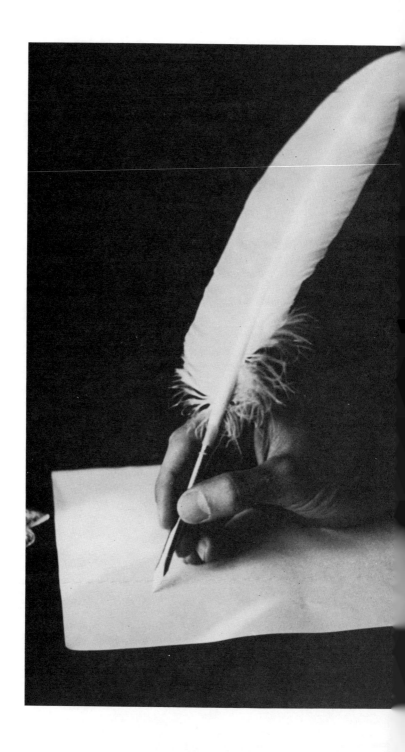

Language and Laterality

THE SPEAKER, GERMANICUS.

Mine hand also hath laid the foundation of the earth,

and my right hand hath spanned the heavens:

ISAIAH 48, 13

■ Language and Laterality

Whatever controversies continue to appear about where language is located in the brain, the problem can never be dissociated from laterality. This is so much the case that we state clearly, at the outset, that the two problems are one and the same.

Cannot language and laterality in perfecting their interplay, unveil for us the mystery of what it means to be human? The seesaw motion that exists between these two mechanisms exists in all human relationship interreactions.

Articulated human language requires a very elaborate cybernetic control. It implies the presence of a receiver, which need not be singular, but which must be unilateral. The internal liberties allowed by any system which does not conform to this fundamental requirement would permit multiple errors to occur, thus preventing the normal speech rhythm flow common to human beings. Language and the need to control it created the need to construct laterality. This lateralization applies first to sensory control of our self-listening; it makes us conscious of our language and breaks away from automatic processes that can only lead to a purely expressive language. This control occurs at the first level of our sensory awareness and is known as *gnosis*, as distinct from unconscious or, to some extent, automatic perception. Any act cybernetically dependent on this control is designated *praxis*, or acquired act, as distinct from instinctive, involuntary acts.

Therefore, both knowledge and conscious gesture must be distinguished, and they depend upon unilateral control. Thus a right-hander, for example, executes all his praxial, learned acts under the control of his right gnosis, including in this regulation the gestures of the left side of the body. The lack of precision, the clumsiness that appears, is only the translation of errors inherent to excessive straining of that control.

Our entire being is thus controlled by a single side, and this we owe to language.

To assume that a functional asymmetry has been acquired in the course of human development is to reaffirm the idea that the two cerebral hemispheres have different activities.

There is an idea suggested by an abuse of language that only one side — the right — is favored, while the other is left, so to speak, a burdensome appendage that we drag along unwillingly. We would like to state our opposition to that idea in the strongest terms. The left is every bit as indispensable to the structure of our asymmetry as the right. The term "dominant" inputes an active role to one side, but the role attributed to the other side is just as noble; it is simply less demonstrative, as it operates in the shadow of the other. Analysis of the information received by the dominant side depends on the mechanism of the non-dominant side and the way it puts things into effect. The practiced execution that seems only to come out of decisions of the dominant side is organized out of the non-dominant side's integrating response. If we wanted to conform to the reality we are proposing, i.e., the hypothesis just put forth, the main or dominant half of the brain could well be called the "executor" while the opposite side would become in our description the "integrator." One supplies the active response; the other, the analogical response.

This approach to the problem is more consistent with our current knowledge of the functional mechanics of the brain. The two hemispheres do not actually play the same role, particularly where the body is concerned. As reported by Ajuriaguerra and Hecaen in their work *Méconnaissances et hallucinations corporelles [Misconceptions and hallucinations of the body]*, the pathology of the right brain bears no resemblance to the pathology of the left brain. On the gnosic plane, for example, an injury to the right brain induces a loss of gnosis on the left side of the body, or bodily hemiagnosia or, more precisely, hemiasomatognosia. Loss of consciousness of the left side goes so far as to include ignorance of the very malfunction that has afflicted the individual. Furthermore — and this is always disconcerting to the observer — in spite of the terrible physiological disorder that results from this pathological alteration, the subject remains cheerful and euphoric.

An entirely different clinical aspect is presented by a patient affected by an identical lesion of the left brain. Aside even from any language problems that may occur, the subject is morose, unmotivated, and no longer has consciousness of his body as a whole; his asomatognosia is all-pervasive. In this case the body is completely deprived of its informative capacity, which is the undisputed domain of the right side of the body that is controlled by the left brain, which in this particular case study is diseased. If sensory information ceases to be available, the right brain no longer has anything to analyze, still less to integrate, and its response is nil. In sum, the executive development of all our praxes is equal and proportional to the degree to which the gnoses that control them have been perfected.

A dialogue is established between our two halves of our brain, and from that dialogue arise many systems of regulation and of analogical memory storage.

We have thus deliberately defined a gnosial and praxial (knowing and acting) brain, the left, and a referential brain, the right, whose main role is to allow us to work out that gnosia and praxis.

No doubt it is in the interpretation of the dialogue between the two hemispheres, which maintains a state of permanent respective wakefulness in our brain, that we will one day unravel the mysteries of our transcendent human species.

For the sake of absolute clarity we would like to reiterate our belief that to us it seems likely that all gnosis and praxis does depend solely on the left brain. Thus a movement executed with the right hand is obviously under the effective command of the left brain, but a praxial movement executed by the left hand likewise depends on the same mechanism; it is regulated by the tandem: left brain receiver and executor vs. right brain analyzer and integrator.

A movement voluntarily made by the right hand is obviously more rapidly executed than it would be with the left hand, which is cybernetically more difficult to reach, the voluntary or praxial movements being in fact only the controlled utilization of our automatic movements. Automatic movements are what remain under the unified command of both our separate brain halves together. The rest is dependent on the presence of the concept left-brain vs. right-brain such as we have defined it.

From our clinical and laboratory work we can confidently advance and defend our point of view.

All absence of perfectly developed language is generally accompanied by undetermined or badly determined laterality. In the days and weeks that follow, language education immediately brings out a very striking evolution in the praxial movements and a simultaneous appearance of gnosial laterality. When the same becomes homogeneous, praxial maturation occurs, with the result that one side acquires greater dexterity.

As a rule the right side brightens up on the gnosial level when we set about elaborating awareness of language. This result is obtained through language alone, without any other educational maneuver.

But if a withdrawal movement is experienced during this development or some resistance gets in the way, we witness an inversion of the gnosial image. The left side then seems to become the dominant sensory side. The disorders that follow from this can be minimized by encouraging praxis on the left side. With only a few exceptions, this appearance of dominant left-handedness seems, however, to be an anomaly, a psychological or psychosensory withdrawal. It marks a stop or a deviation in the natural maturing of gnosial development. Such a left-hander remains slow, absent, given to daydreaming, inhibited when faced with movements that are too fast, often drawn into rhythms that are no doubt imposed on him by uncontrolled and instinctive acts. His regulation lacks awareness and is too complicated. The load which converges on his Self demands that he make an effort of almost insurmountable proportions; more than anyone, he has to give all of himself to obtain a result that is often insignificant. The whole way in which he regulates himself is cybernetically unsustainable, short of a gigantic effort. The body image conveyed by the language of other people reaches him reversed on itself. He has to be continuously turning it back around the right way.

The left-brain/right-brain bloc thus functions identically in operation to the right-handed brain. Cerebral left-sidedness is truly an exception, which can only be confirmed after a long examination followed by education through language over several weeks, accompanied by an initiation of the body schema.

The cases of two youngsters afflicted with serious language difficulties will give a still better understanding of what we have thus far argued.

1. The first case has to do with a child aged twelve, academically very backward, having extreme difficulties in reading and writing, typically dyslexic and dysorthographic, with no vocabulary, sensorially left-dominant eye, writing sometimes with the left

hand, sometimes with the right, according to the decision of the latest physician or pedagogist consulted, in short, totally deaf on the left side.

We are struck immediately by the awkwardness of all his movements and even by the sense of discomfort evident in all his attitudes; his language is poor in verbal expressions; his voice is monotonous, without timbre. In addition, the act of speaking considerably exaggerates an already noticeable facial asymmetry which gives his left side complete amimia [a lack of expressiveness]. The overall results of a general examination evidences left motor insufficiency. Multiple examinations carried out on this young boy by numerous colleagues invariably ended in a diagnosis of "meningeal hemorrhage" that occurred at birth. This was undoubtedly the most probable hypothesis.

Without committing ourselves on whether re-education will be successful, we advise the family that we will try reactivation of the right side. Our decision, which currently dates back two and a half years, corresponded to the classic conception of right-handedness and left-handedness. Since our young subject who was deprived of language seemed to have been afflicted at birth by a left hemiplegia (damage to the right side of the brain), which had certainly badly regressed, especially on the level of motor control, it was logical to guess that he was left-handed and that his language center, located in principle in the right brain, had been damaged. The re-education we undertook at that time on the right side had only one goal: to awaken a cortical order in the left brain that might be able to supplement the deficient right-hand center.

So off we go, confident in our hypothesis, soon encouraged by the prodigiously rapid improvement shown by our young patient. We are somewhat astonished to find, however, that hearing tests taken some twenty days later show an extraordinary comeback in his hearing sensitivity on the left. Were we mistaken? Did we just awaken left-handedness? Has the right cortical center been activated? The problem remains unsolved, but that fact is of secondary importance since we can now send our young subject back to his school environment. The results prove to be surprising in every respect. The child can now complete his final term in the fifth grade without apparent difficulty.

What is most impressive is that our young boy is so euphoric, in such good spirits, and demonstrates such enthusiasm. The parents, the teachers, everyone remarks on it.

The first trimester of the following school year also starts out smoothly. The beginning of the second school trimester, however, is marked by a real setback. Inactivity, dreaminess, and slowness have recaptured our young schoolboy, so much so that one wonders whether he will have to be taken out of school. At about that same time we get him back. All the tests clearly show serious regression. His left hearing sensitivity has crashed again, although it has not entirely disappeared.

We decide to take him back daily for re-education and on the strength of our first experience we focus him on the left; we begin to re-educate his left hearing and for greater efficacy, we ask him to write with the left hand. The results are spectacular. In a few days his left handwriting becomes equivalent to his right, and his left hearing undergoes considerable improvement, to within normal limits.

Yet much to our surprise, the control examination shows our young boy to be more alert, more open, with mobile features on both sides, a gnosic right-hander, right-handed of eye and ear.

Without influencing him we ask him to practice knowledge of laterality on himself and very rapidly his body schema becomes fixed normally like everyone else, namely on the right; a few days later he becomes praxic on the right.

Since then the child has gone back to school and can follow school work without difficulty. It may be noted that his performance tests and verbal tests, taken at six-month intervals, have increased successively from 90 to 96 and have finally reached 107.

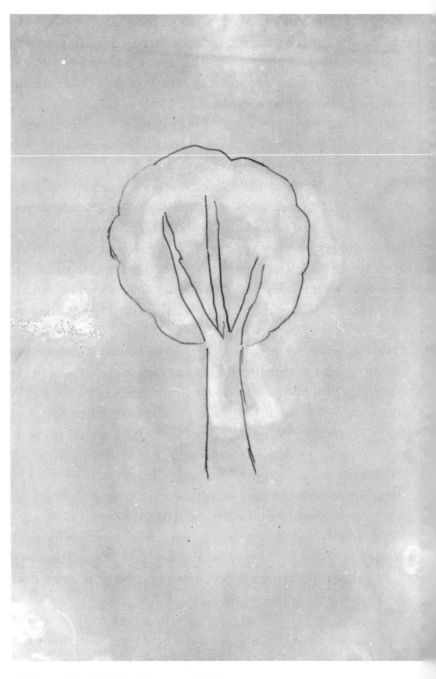

FIGURE 14. TREE DRAWN BEFORE RE-EDUCATION.

FIGURE 15. TREE DRAWN BY THE SAME CHILD AFTER FIFTEEN HOURS OF AUDIOVOCAL CONDITIONING.

FIGURE 16. PICTURE OF THE FAMILY DRAWN BY THE SAME CHILD BEFORE RE-EDUCATION.

2. The second case study concerns the language re-education we undertook with a twenty-year-old young man, who was referred to us by a rehabilitation center for hemiplegics. His infirmity, which occurred at birth, is located on the left. His language skills are considerable. To tell the truth, language is nonexistent despite well-managed attempts at re-education. Following traditional concepts, the initial aphasia has suggested the hypothesis that this young man is left-handed. It is therefore correct to surmise that the initial lesions affecting his right brain have damaged his language faculty.

Audiometric examination leads the same way and supports the clinical picture by revealing profound deafness on the left.

le père

la mère

la fille et ma sœur

FIGURE 17. PICTURE OF THE FAMILY DRAWN BY THE SAME CHILD AFTER FIFTEEN HOURS OF AUDIOVOCAL CONDITIONING.

Everything is there in its ideal combination. On the strength of the preceding case we undertake re-education of his left hearing, which is spectacularly reawakened. From then on, language takes form rapidly and improves in accuracy; the articulatory disorders disappear progressively, while comprehension increases day by day; we have done as much as we can for him, having obtained the best we could hope for.

However, four or five months after the end of the treatment he turns up again and we note a clear regression. The tests we make show total auditory ambivalence, ambiacousia, which is surprising, to say the least, in this confirmed left-hander. We attempt language re-education on the right with right audio-corporeal initiation. In a few days the results amply surpass anything we had previously achieved. Intelligibility of language in this young man may be considered as acquired in total, while his elocution has become fluid, rapid and normal, replacing the slow and imprecise left-hander's language he had revealed at the start.

We have chosen two serious pathological cases, but these techniques are applicable to any minor cases that reveal the same disorders, arising from the non-structured "language and laterality." This symbiosis can only be realized in so far as our sensory receivers are of good quality.

To become convinced of these facts, it is sufficient to consider language problems without mentioning rhythm problems. Besides, these are explained elsewhere as related to cybernetics and manifested in articulation or pronunciation. They all testify to the poor quality of the auditory receiver we are using.

The intelligibility of what is sent and repeated assures us of the speaker's ability to regulate language. But what difficulties we encounter, what distortions we hear, how many spelling errors appear and reappear in spite of all the exercises repeated to the exhaustion of both student and teacher. The faithful reproduction of a spelling error is nothing but the accurate translation of the sound as it has been perceived, as it has been registered and as it has been memorized. Corrective education of hearing is sufficient to eliminate the bad integration made visible by writing; no other procedures are necessary. Similarly, articulatory disorders on the phonation level have an identical origin, and their treatment involves the same techniques.

A deeper and even more troublesome problem exists, which manifests itself in difficulties related to reading. The blanket term "dyslexia" has been adopted to cover all its clinical forms. The subject may be affected to such a degree that he cannot read at all. The blockage goes hand in hand with malfunction of our two auditory receivers, which become ambivalent upon trying to integrate phonemes hitting any given frequency band. Thus words are destroyed and piled together, syllables are inverted. It goes without saying that one cannot comprehend the text at any given moment. Here again education of auditory laterality can be extremely beneficial. Improvement is rapid, and sometimes spectacular.

To summarize, in the application of current techniques, we can hope to give a new chance to crystalize to that complex but fragile organization, which holds in its power both body and language.

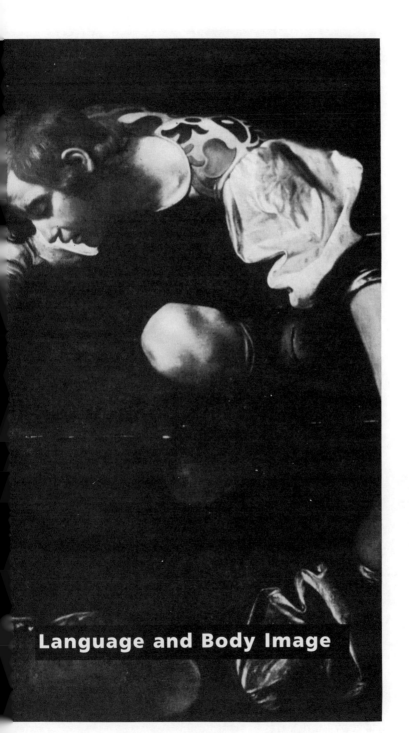

Language and Body Image

THE ENTIRE BODY PARTICIPATES IN EXPRESSION.

The deepest thing in man
is his skin.
VALERY, L'IDÉE FIXE

■ Language and Body Image

Perhaps the best definition of our concept of language is communication with another through the intermediary of Self. When we speak, no one is more completely informed than ourselves! To communicate successfully we have to use our whole body, because that is where our world begins. First and foremost, it is our own body that must believe in the truthfulness of our discourse. Our body lends itself to this game like a resounding instrument, and words play on it with multiple chords and infinite variations. The body obeys all the wanderings of our thoughts with incredible suppleness.

The human body is the instrument of language, and human language is the song that makes it resound. Man's body is the instrument man's thought uses to speak.

The entire body participates in expression, in very simple and direct ways. The body contributes to expression through looks, through mime, through gesture, through attitude, through the whole of our living and dynamic being. The body controls expression by hearing, by sight, by skin, by all senses that have been sharpened for one purpose ever since our initiation into the world of sound — the enhancement of our humanity.

We transmit language through our whole body. What we

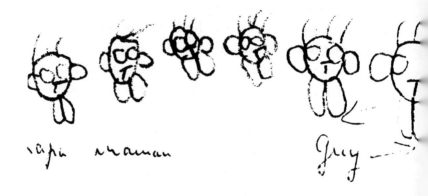

FIGURE 18. PICTURE OF A MAN AND FAMILY DRAWN BEFORE RE-EDUCATION.

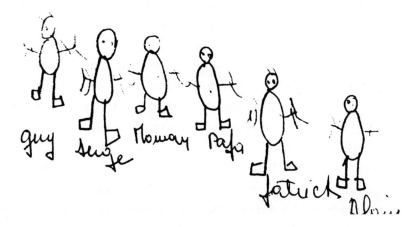

FIGURE 19. PICTURE DRAWN BY THE SAME CHILD AFTER FIFTEEN HOURS OF AUDIOVOCAL CONDITIONING.

intend to communicate is neither sounds, words, phrases, nor acoustic phenomena; they are instead profoundly felt sensations experienced within our sensory neurons, chords that our speech has sounded upon us with persuasion, precision, warmth, and enthusiasm.

What we want is to mark as our own those tactile chords that speech plays on our sensory keyboard.

We know vaguely and instinctively that these same chords will be transmitted to our listener. If he is caught up in our game he cannot help but use his whole body to interpret and translate us. He unconsciously matches his expression-sensing apparatus to ours, while we keep him in resonance by means of our own chords.

To let our body sing is to transmit to other people our proprioceptive sensations. If the song is ample and harmonious, if it is supple and easily produced, it will transmit the warmth of a calm and powerful thoracic expansion; if it is narrow and strained, it will imprison us within the same anguish that blocks its emission.

Our body image is constantly formed by our spoken words, sculpted and drawn in its finest detail by our sonic caresses.

We speak to please ourselves. We surround ourselves with an acoustic mirror, the better to see and know ourselves. Our language models itself on our body, as that body defines itself in us, as we conceive of it through the information of our senses. A relative interaction here reflects our own way of communicating with ourselves. Our choice of control, the virtuosity with which we learn to play the whole range of our sensory keyboard, will determine our means of obtaining information, which in turn will determine our means of control. A series of chain reactions, all resulting from their common interreactions, will thus unfold, accelerate, and enrich itself.

As a reflection of our speech, the image of our body is projected into space to the exact extent that the image of our speech springs from the image of our body.

Our bodily knowledge, sum of the knowledge of our means of expression, will be solidly structured in proportion as it adheres to thought, in so far as such adherence is humanly possible.

The resulting pyramidal and dynamic form of the Self that springs from this rests on the most substantively and unconsciously automatic corporeal bases. Superposed on it is the wise and fragile scaffolding of sensory control, master of the voluntary act, master of regulation, originator of laterality, which is the dynamic force centralizing the act of control.

Clinical work offers us a case in point: a seven-year-old child was referred to us by a colleague, a pediatrician and psychiatrist, for considerable retardation in language associated with a serious intellectual deficit. Examination revealed a child of normal constitution, if anything rather tall for his age, but, puffy-faced and of poor mobility, quite unruly in his behavior, and absolutely incapable of making himself understood, as all his words were mispronounced. Study of his laterality revealed bilateral responses, which appeared to be subject to chance and the boy's whim. When we gave him a drawing test and asked him to draw a man, we observed a circle with a central spot: the global representation of his Self without differentiation of any part of his body. We decided to undertake an education of his language. As a result of this education, which was carried out under specified conditions with the help of electronic filters, we noted language development in the child, despite his low intelligence quotient. At the end of three months his language became intelligible, right-handedness appeared, and the child's drawings of a man assured us of his progress in body awareness. Now a head surmounts the body, arms and legs freed themselves from the body, and hands and feet completed the sketch. We returned the child to his family at that time, unaware that he was to stay two or three days with a grandmother who was unconvinced or uninformed about our techniques. In a short time she made a few remarks or reprimands that were no doubt quite sensible as instruction, but catastrophic for the psycho-sensory and psycho-motor faculties we had tried to awaken in our little child; within a few hours his language fell apart as if by a spell. Nothing was left of what we had built. Laterality was replaced by the initial ambivalence, while the body schema was again indicated in drawing by a poorly defined circle without differentiation of any kind. Without losing courage we took back our little student. Rapidly, in a few days, everything was built up again, but this time we took the precaution of instructing the family about what to do.

Better than a long lecture, this experimental reconstruction of language demonstrates the parallel evolution of the double acquisition of speech and body image.

It is in this reincarnation of the word that the genius of language is born. As Father Jousse says, its rhythm and balance depend on it; its phraseology is confirmed by it; its syntax is founded on it; last but not least, its memorization depends on it.

From language and from language alone arises the conscious speaking body. But one cannot build such a magnificent edifice without incurring some risk: the danger is in the excessive pleasure we take in listening to ourselves. It is easy to forget what we meant to say, seeking only to admire the narcissistic image of self in the words, words that become meaningless, empty of thought. The myth of The Tower of Babel acquires new force in this context. Everyone in the story used language only in order to envision his own body, and in the end this cult of the individual destroyed all hope that we had of understanding each other and of communicating the seeds of thought, which is both unique and universal.

We are approaching the end of this brief tour of the subject of hearing and language, and we find ourselves reluctant to abandon the reader.

We would like to keep him with us, let him touch with his fingers what we have described, let him experience by ever-renewed example each of our chapters, elaborate for him in detail the clinical and therapeutic characteristics only touched upon in these pages. In short, we wish that by practicing all these techniques, where speech reigns supreme, our reader would become initiated into the world of language that completely absorbs all those who venture into it. But those who speak the same language are never completely separated from one another, and happily since everything hasn't yet been said, we are left with the best of encouragements that there will be a next time, another book.

Have we managed to involve the reader in our subject? Will he know how to use his physical understanding to interpret us, to translate us into the language of his body? Are our own convictions strong enough to convey to him in the rhythm of these resonances what we would like him to feel? Shall we hear him argue in his turn, with the same enthusiasm: "When you speak, sound pours from your mouth like water overflowing from a basin. It inundates and spreads over your whole body. Without your conscious awareness, but nonetheless assuredly, syllable waves break and wash over you. Your entire body surface marks their progress through the skin's sensitivity, as if controlled by a keyboard that is receptive to acoustic touch."

The Ideal of the Sage: One ear cocked to listen.

■ Postscript 1990

Although it has been almost thirty years since this book was first printed, no modifications are required to that 1963 edition. However, we have updated the research that since then has been achieved in the fields of auditory physiology and psycholinguistics.

As time passes, the ear seems to be gaining the recognition it deserves. By developing a listening capability, it places itself at the service of that extraordinary faculty which transforms a man into a human being. With this new self-monitoring approach, the ear has made itself a quite exceptional and essential apparatus dedicated to listening dynamics.

Rather than a conclusion, this postscript marks the end of one phase. Research sustained by theoretical knowledge throws new light on the numerous fields of study related to listening, language, and communication. Within this perspective one can glimpse the degree to which infinite numbers of application areas overlap in linguistics, psychology and psychiatry, psychosomatics, and semantics.

To start, one must be thoroughly conversant with the ideas that gave birth to this book and to have had the opportunity to comment on them before accepting the arguments or evaluating their potential.

■ The Integrators

Listening is everything. And every part of man is an ear, even though he doesn't often devote himself to this particular function.

Following the discovery of the audio-vocal loops in 1947, I discovered other audiolinguistic and audiocorporeal circuits that have since become an integral part of the language field. A complete "neuronal system" emerged, which upon analysis indicated a functional anatomy that would have significant practical consequences.

In fact, if you have language acquisition as a guideline, it will be much easier to penetrate into different levels of the nervous system. This can only be achieved with help of the internal ear's vestibulo-cochlear components and in its bodily implications. These have led us to the study of what I refer to as the "integrators."

Used by man to govern the politics of his verbal and nonverbal communication, these diverse cybernetic complexes came to light when it became evident that the counterreactions could be regrouped into different networks. These networks would associate muscular command paths with those of sensory responses related to the corresponding territories.

The neural tree is composed of four major integrators, which became known in terms of their phylogenetic and ontogenetic history. The order established responds to the many exigencies called into play by the needs of the moment. Beginning with the earliest discovery and moving to the most recent, we discover:

1. The vestibular integrator
2. The olfactory integrator
3. The visual integrator
4. The cochlear integrator

The *vestibular integrator* governs the automatic "dynamic structure" by means of a protopathic neural structure, which is outside the realm of consciousness. Over the course of its evolution it progressively takes over all motor functions until it controls all movement of the diverse muscle groups. It both ensures motion and makes standing still possible. It is, in reality, the functional, primitive brain that coordinates all bodily functions, giving it the further designation of "somatic integrator." It becomes more complex as one follows its development to discover the functional addition of the archeo- and then of the paleocerebellum. One can then justifiably envision its blossoming into the crown of the tree of the nervous system, in other words, the brain. This integrator is all the more important because it acts as the base element of subsequent structure. It will simultaneously become the mainstay of and servant to the other integrators.

The *olfactory integrator*, dominant in the rhinencephalon, is the "central" detector for fish species, for example, for whom the sense of smell is the primary means of connecting with their surroundings. It is the organ that enables them to find their way. The vestibular integrator will direct it on demand to wherever it wants to go. An obvious interdependence exists between the two integrators. But as has been previously stated, the power for the assembly is and remains the group commanded by the vestibular apparatus, which is composed of the utricle with its semicircular canals and of the saccule.

The *visual integrator* soon takes over. Its relationship of control over the vestibule is identical to that used up until then by its predecessor. Sight gradually replaces the sense of smell. It is initially monocular, from the time of the fish up to that of the birds. Then it becomes binocular among mammals. The optical ensemble predominates here.

The *cochlear integrator* follows, and it radically changes all previous relationships between the various neuronal components. The cochlea takes control of the system and, in conjunction with the vestibule, progressively induces man's characteristic upright posture, verticality. Only man benefits from this integration; no other animal has achieved it. From the time he is able to recognize another person through sound, he also discovers himself through the spoken word. A dialectic is thus established between the vestibule and the cochlea that leads man on through the course of his development.

In effect, these two neuronal ensembles will work synergistically to realize what we call the "listening posture." This posture allows man to be a vibrating antenna attentively receptive to all information coming to him from the universe, the environment, and his own body. This posture, which is so characteristic of the human species in relation to, among other things, verticality, dexterity, the hand's freedom of movement, and language, requires that the cochlea establish a dialogue with the vestibule, so as to spatially position itself. After this readjustment, accomplished through the integrators, man can easily express the thoughts that occur to him.

These neuronic arrangements, which have been activated in order to reach the lofty peaks of verbalization, are explained in some of my other works. It will suffice here to present drawings illustrating the two main arrangements and showing the different circuits followed by the afferent and efferent nerve fibers, at once sensorial and motor. It is precisely these sensorimotor groups, veritable networks that I have labeled "integrators" to denote their functional unity.

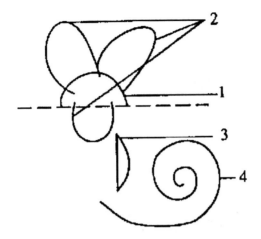

FIGURE 20. LISTENING POSTURE
1. UTRICLE 2. SEMICIRCULAR CANALS 3. SACCULE 4. COCHLEA

The vestibular integrator can be represented as follows:

- The vestibule (V) sends to the body (B) the vestibular nerve (VN), which sends an extrapyramidal nerve ending to the muscles.
- The body (B) ensures the return of sensory information via two different routes, Flechsig's fasciculi (FF) and Gowers' tract (GT), which lead off toward the paleocerebellum (PC).
- The paleocerebellum (PC) is the relay that receives sensory information for the vestibule (V) after it passes through another relay, the archeocerebellum (AC).
- The passage from one relay (AC) to the other (PC) is achieved through the network woven by Purkinje cells (P).
- Two complimentary fasciculi, one of which passes through the red nucleus (RN) and the other through the bulbar olivary body (BO), reinforce this group of integrators.

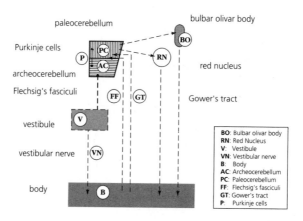

FIGURE 21. VESTIBULAR INTEGRATOR

The cochlear integrator leaves the cochlear analyzer (Co) and moves toward the temporal cortex (TC) passing through the posterior section of the thalamus (T).

- From the temporal cortex (TC) the information assembles and moves toward the nucleus of the pons (NP), then it converges on the neocerebellum (NC).
- It returns to the frontal cortex (FC) and the parietal cortex (PC) passing through the central area of the thalamus (T).
- This results in the formation of a large cortical circuit that stores the information within the brain as a whole.
- The body becomes involved due to a nerve branch serving the red nucleus (RN), which sends a fasciculus toward the body (B).
- The vestibule is constantly concerned with the network formed by the Purkinje cells functionally reuniting the neocerebellum (NC) with the two other cerebellum regions, the archeocerebellum (AC), and the paleocerebellum (PC).

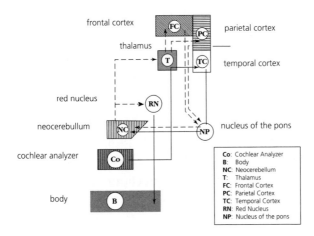

frontal cortex

parietal cortex

thalamus

temporal cortex

red nucleus

neocerebullum

nucleus of the pons

cochlear analyzer

Co: Cochlear Analyzer
B: Body
NC: Neocerebellum
T: Thalamus
FC: Frontal Cortex
PC: Parietal Cortex
TC: Temporal Cortex
RN: Red Nucleus
NP: Nucleus of the pons

body

FIGURE 22. COCHLEAR INTEGRATOR

■ A New Approach to Auditory Physiology

After this quick overview of the intimate relationships between the ear, body, and language, we can now tackle a subject which is at the heart of our preoccupations — the functioning of the human ear.

Various different theories advanced over the past century by researchers such as Helmholtz have necessitated a more detailed study of the awesome problems posed by auditory physiology. Their hypotheses, long since accepted by the medical world, especially in oto-rhino-laryngology circles, have been pushed even further these past few decades, especially by Békésy, but researchers have encountered impasses, and other investigations have proved their chosen path is not the right one.

We thus found it necessary to re-examine how the human ear functions and to study how the sonic impulse travels from the external auditory canal to the internal ear. How do the acoustic vibrations reach the labyrinth, that privileged place where semantic information is distilled, which is also the center of communication par excellence?

Some novel concepts will be put forward to explain the route traveled by sound and to answer the questions currently being asked by some ear, nose and throat (ENT) specialists. One cannot simply follow the trail of one's predecessors without searching out the underlying basis of the theories they proposed, even more so as certain pathologies, such as Ménière's, seem to provide us with clues which point in unexpected directions. In reality, the ear functions in exactly the opposite manner to what was previously believed.

A detailed description of the hearing mechanism will not be presented here because a highly specialized discourse is not needed. Any reader who is interested will find such an analysis in several of my other books. Presented here in a simplified manner are the results of our auditory physiology research.

As we can see, sound follows one of two different paths, according to whether one embraces Békésy's proposed route or the one I suggest. In Békésy's hypothesis, sound moves along the anatomical bridge created by the ossicular chain consisting of the hammer, anvil, and stirrup. This conception stands up poorly to functional analysis. In the second case, the one that we have subjected to experimentation, the peripheral bone that surrounds the tympanic membrane, especially the lower area, conducts the sound toward the inner ear. From this starting point it is easy to explain how the inner ear works.

■ Genetic Linguistics

The research concerning prenatal hearing that we published in the first edition of this book was confirmed in the 1960s, and now constitutes a part of the body of established research relating to prenatal life.

In 1953, I was given the opportunity to prove this new concept — which my contemporaries considered to be revolutionary, if not provocative — and I was drawn into the study of a highly specialized dimension of language, namely, genetic linguistics.

This aforementioned dimension is actually the very origin of linguistics. Physiological support is found in an ontogenesis that is relatively easy to explore. Genetic linguistics reveals the development of an entire relational dynamic that comes into play around a psycho-physiological structure. This in none other than the first linguistic structure upon which the world's languages imprint themselves and find their real origin.

Much has been said about this primordial source as we have searched for the characteristics of the original mother tongue. But research has floundered on numerous imponderables, and some research has even contributed a kind of sclerosis. No matter how beautiful it may be, however pure it may seem to be, however sacred it is believed to be, this language that has been so desperately sought after has vanished. It was its destiny to die. Sanskrit, a wonderful linguistic fossil, is a classic example. Ancient Greek gave way to Modern Greek. And Latin gave rise to the Romance languages, before fading from the memory of men.

A new and significant concept evolved in 1953 from the evidence of intrauterine listening, which I was able to describe. I demonstrated that from the first weeks of prenatal life the embryo-fetus enters into an acoustic-sonic relationship with its mother. The auricular apparatus is perfectly and completely formed after four and a half months in the uterus. Only the development of the external ear remains to be completed after birth.

The neurological mechanisms of this organ, which is so precociously conceived, develop especially quickly. The vestibulo-cochlear nerves are operative or myelinized after five and a half

FIGURE 23. PASSAGE OF SOUND: HELMHOLTZ-BÉKÉSY CONCEPTION

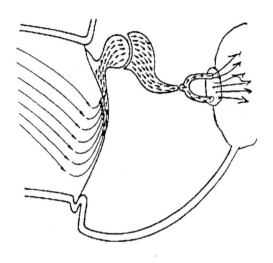

FIGURE 24. PASSAGE OF SOUND: TOMATIS CONCEPTION

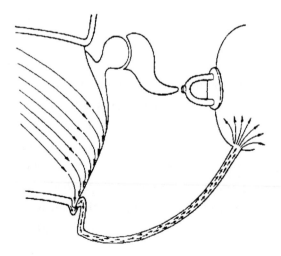

months of intrauterine life. By an equally precious myelinization, the auditory area of the temporal brain is fully active at birth. This is far in advance of the development of the other sensory organs.

By a process that may seem paradoxical, the study of language, so closely tied to that of audition, brings us back to the search for these essential and primordial sources. Is the first language not already established in the mother's womb? Undoubtedly in the coming years numerous investigations in this newly explored field will bear fruit, such as that which revealed the genesis of the linguistic structures which the fetal ear is already able to perceive. Is the fetal ear not capable of registering the basis and fundamentals of the most elementary form of language, which is expressed in babbling and is primarily reserved for the mother? The true maternal language is the same in all corners of the world, across all ethnic boundaries.

Genetic linguistics will undoubtedly end the futile search for the generator of all languages, the first language. There is no doubt that this unique point of departure does exist. Everyone has experienced it in the course of elaborating his or her own language. Ontogenesis provides each and every human being with an extraordinary philogenetic existential outline, which allows him in the course of one lifetime to re-experience this incredible adventure, leading him through time from the beginning of creation toward the creature he has now become.

Moreover, it is creation itself that speaks through him, providing he is not too caught up in overwhelming daily preoccupations. But it is by using his own speech that man integrates himself into this universe that creates him, envelops him, and carries him along. Man is a unique, thinking entity mirroring the cosmos; he is capable of perceiving everything in this world in the form of thought crystallized by verbalization.

The spoken and perceived word, together with the act of listening to the rhythm of the first language, henceforth gives way to a reality and permanently generates the first creative impulse. Nothing comes closer to the primordial infinite released by the Word than the Logos when it has once again set off on the human adventure within the uterine universe.

Eternal repetition. Eternal rejuvenation. The linguistic evolution finds its meaning and roots in the very depths of genetic tradition. This evolution benefits from archaic memory, constantly enriched and progressively revised by the laws of exchange with the environment. It is the reflection of a fundamental homeostasis, which simultaneously manages the course of life and its existential expression.

As one might imagine, these past thirty years have been rich in acquisitions. Having discovered how the nervous system functions through the vestibular, visual, and cochlear integrators, we can now understand how the listening mechanism functions and develop a new approach to auditory physiology and the study of the mechanisms of the human ear.

We are well aware of how significant a role we attribute to this organ, which is why we felt that it was necessary, even essential, to understand how it functions. We thought it equally important to show how its exceptional sensitivity allows it to completely respond to the opening or closing modes induced by diverse psychological states.

In this way the function of hearing was transcended to achieve the remarkable capacity of listening. What then is this famous capacity? It is nothing less than the faculty of receiving sounds, experiencing them, appreciating them, recognizing them, and giving them a significance, a value. It is then possible to extract from one word the weight and the dimensions that characterize it, that is to say, to evaluate its quantity and quality, its intensity, its components, its frequency structure, etc. Moreover, for every perceived sound that is accepted and thus digested, classified, and stored, a recurrent and active memory interplay determines, in the course of repetition, a significant meaning for it. In short, this capacity we have spoken of classifies it within the vast catalog of acoustic memory.

Within this dynamic of listening, we will know how to distinguish noise, music, electro-acoustic experiences that are perhaps overgenerously referred to as music and communicative sounds. A sonic seed of this kind, which grows in this infinite vibrating universe, will allow the establishment of a complete series of specific sounds, which can be reproduced at leisure within the linguistic conditions that are imposed by the network of the listening canals. It is at this point that language is born, a language that truly characterizes a nation, an ethnic group, a land, an atmosphere, an acoustic with its own elective frequencies or, better yet, its own specific preferential resonances…in short, all that sustains communication.

■ Listening and Communication

Blessed with our now familiar system of neural organization, which is composed of different integrators — vestibular (or somatic), visual (or "reading head"), cochlear (or linguistic) — man develops in his optimal dimension, that which permits him to finally utilize his fundamental potential. There is no longer any need to hope for a miracle, for a superman of some kind to burst forth rich with a new genetic capital, forerunner of a more elaborate nervous system. Let us be content to fully use that which has been so generously offered to us by an overabundant nature and a creation that invites us to participate in its evolving adventure.

The relationship of "being on the same wavelength" with the other, that is to say, the desired systemic meeting, is far from being attained. Daily experience confirms this. Only a small number of people are privileged to understand that the great communication, which man is urged to take part in, invites him to converse with the universe itself. This privileged relationship with the Logos thus permits him to develop his creativity, the real essence of ontological poetry, the invisible and present source from which vitality itself springs. Intuition manifests itself at this point, a kind of spark that ignites and develops productivity in order to ensure progress and to create an elevation toward the spheres where the breath of the creative spirit transforms the person who allows himself to be filled with it.

Thus man, whose development has led him to be simultaneously the "talker," the "listener," and the "communicator," attains verticality thanks to the receptive antenna that he gradually becomes. He also learns how to increase his sensitivity, to manage his feelings, to intensify his emotions in regard to all that is, to that which he himself represents, and to that which surrounds him. He manages thus to juggle his sensibility and emotionalism, two parameters that negatively affect and immobilize activity pertinent to creativity. They paralyze or dissolve objectivity and destroy judgment, while enclosing perception in an incoherent, irrational, colored subjectivity.

In this way a person can lose his resonances. Overshadowed in some way, he finds it impossible to express himself using the normal receiver/transmitter system. More or less polluted, this system falls prey to malfunctioning, the consequences of which can quickly be evaluated. As they involve listening, they will be varied. Without the ability to listen, there is no communication. Without communication, there is no valid social life. In short, this heralds the slippery slope toward alienation.

■ Listening and Consciousness

Happily, man is not an island. His autonomy can be completely attained only if he knows how to cast his eyes about him to the fullest extent, and he must do so if he is to live out his destiny to the fullest. At that point, his dependencies, constraints, accumulated events that were more or less accepted or held back disappear, in short, all that creates his psychoanalytical universe. It will be necessary to allow them to settle, in order to rediscover the necessary supra-analytical transparency that will allow the stream of consciousness to illuminate the shady areas, so that darkness diminishes under the flood of light.

This discourse may appear strange, unusual, even too idealistic. Nevertheless, the awareness that ascetics have sought throughout history, which has always remained out of reach to man, today *is* accessible to him. Only he who does not know the keys that allow him to follow such a path gets lost and goes astray. It is important to demystify this process, to remove from it its mysterious, esoteric, secret, and occult side, which encourages certain people to be elitist to the detriment of others. The truth is that there are scarcely any people "chosen," save those who have the good fortune of listening.

Doorway to consciousness, listening is also the doorway to common sense, and even to discernment. But everything invites us to confuse facts, knowledge, and conscience these days. An expert may only see what he has learned and still be removed from reality. In much the same way, he can be wrapped up in his field of science to the extent that he exists only by and within it, without any perception of the real world. Any exaggerated or narrow focus on reality can lead to prejudice. When a theoretician needs to go into depth in order to arrive at some fundamental conclusions, these same conclusions can risk keeping him within the limits of his own convictions. Whereas, for scientists belonging to other disciplines, these conclusions would merely represent a few more pieces of the jigsaw puzzle that make up the overall world order.

It goes without saying that a 180-degree diaphragmatic opening would not be sufficient. Nor would 360-degrees be, if this were attainable. To obtain a more global vision, the organic neuronal crystal must be able to function in its multidimensional capacity. The brain itself is polyoperational. Unfortunately, an apprenticeship without the support of a real education wears away man's aspirations to the point of letting him believe that he sees because he knows, that he understands because he learns, and that he discovers thanks to his intuitive knowing what the world, the other, and he himself are about.

His baggage is, in fact, an accumulation of knowledge that could be of great help if it were used as a springboard to allow humanity to progress instead of only to advance arguments in his own field. It ought to make it possible for him to participate in all that comes his way, but his experience too often remains overshadowed by hypothesis and theories of all kinds. How many times does knowledge hide evidence behind an impenetrable screen or surround it with a dense halo that hides the whole horizon?

■ Science and Evidence

We have now accumulated quite a few concepts that we would do well to define. Though they are only words, they should evoke within the reader, as much as possible, what the author means by "evidence". Only that which is and cannot fail to be is evident. This does not mean that total authenticity always reveals itself immediately. Sometimes thousands of years are necessary to affirm a piece of evidence.

Right away, this new piece of evidence bothers everyone because it competes with alternative theories and suppresses previous theories, even those that contributed to its crystallization. In truth, these previous theories do not have room to exist because the new evidence is self-sufficient. Science helps us, it is true, to feel comfortable putting numerous things together into extremely elaborate assemblies. If all of the assumptions converge and if all of the supportive theories are subtly guided in one particular direction, which confirms their point of crystallization, then the evidence bursts out. It is truth. This truth is law.

It is well known how few obvious facts exist. They are nevertheless fundamental and permit other expressions of the spirit to be revealed. Everything would assuredly be better in the best of all possible worlds if each piece of evidence was the immediate springboard for other new discoveries. During the flow of time spreading across millennia, an incontestable continuity and a veritable acceleration exist. Nevertheless, it is not easy for every human being to immerse himself in such an evolutionary process.

Perhaps we don't know how to prepare a man to find the essential truth that is rooted in the evidence. Perhaps it will be found embedded within a multitude of traditional, obligatory observations, which have not yet been adequately or correctly examined and have not yielded "the discovery" of that which is. Furthermore, certain individuals are given the opportunity of promoting a piece of knowledge they themselves are trying to acquire, after which they then manifest their autonomy and their power. And yet who has not been struck by the often astoundingly clear, truthful, and authentic retorts made by an illiterate person who is capable of tackling the world in all its reality and of deciphering it with his ears wide open!

■ See and Know

To perceive, which is what science means, is the first prerequisite for knowledge. In this matter, vision seems to be the source of perception. But this visual approach has no right to exist if it has not absorbed and memorized that which it has picked up elsewhere. It has accumulated elements of information in memory reserves, allowing it to conclude in a veritable process of assimilation. It remains to be seen, of course, just how such a memory is absorbed. Is it "incorporated"? Is it a "sign"? Or is the information simply acquired and kept buried in a drawer, then brought out without modification, like data stored on a magnetic tape? If that is the case, it is creating a non-operational, useless data bank with no or very little connection with reality. It has the appearance of science. True knowledge, however, requires an integration, i.e., an analysis, a critical discrimination, an incorporation, an incarnation, in a way. If this process is bypassed, there is no proper understanding of this science, insofar as it remains confused with ontological reality. But does not this remind us in essence of a truth confined within the boundaries of evidence that has been enlightened by consciousness?

To "be born with" means "co-birth," i.e., to reveal oneself to oneself as if marked by a renaissance imprinted with a new dimension. It means to reach a previously unknown level, and to bear witness to a level of consciousness derived from some earlier enlightenment. The more rebirths exist that are regrouped in this way, the more the person discovers himself and uncovers the truth about himself, resulting in the ultimate feeling of crossing over and dwelling in an external memory. In fact, is it not an analogical response that has been incorporated as a reflection of the universe, that same universe that floods through us and is beyond our understanding? From that point on, consciousness, that veritable permanent transfusion that we can only detect under certain conditions, invites us to enter into the field of a reality, of reality itself. This fragmented perception will then make the facts emerge in isolated groups.

As we said previously, absolute truths (which is what facts are) take time to crystallize in our minds. And if they are eternal, it remains no less true that the human brain only emerged after several million years of evolution. Don't forget our difficulty in trying to prove that the earth is round and that it revolves on itself. Without wishing to call to mind the succession of unfortunate events that beset Galileo until the beginning of his journey into the beyond, we can easily imagine the resistance demonstrated by certain scientists who were forced to confront non-illusory truth — a real truth, in short — or, in other words, a fact.

■ Listen and You Will See

Another digression is necessary. We must understand all the implications of "seeing." It is necessary to determine this since, as we have previously said, science implies "to see." All the same, the word "consciousness" multiplied to the infinite implies knowledge in an even more elaborate form. So then "seeing" is everywhere.

And yet, what is it to see, at a level that goes beyond the sense generally attributed to this term? It is to identify, to know, and to recognize; to include this identification with the environment, to add it to the sum of previous acquisitions. To enter it into a world of objects significant in and of themselves, to conceive the unfolding of their respective relationships and as well to reshape them into an easily recalled memory, ready to appear in a series of valued object images.

But without verbalization — a concept intimately tied to listening — will the flow of thought not become muddled? Aren't we going to come across an incredible lack of fluidity? What efforts are we called upon to deploy so that a brain might be able to rediscover the world in its ties with the Logos? Giving it sense allows it to be expressed by reminiscing, which assures the incarnation across the vestibulo-cochlear assembly and the connections this assembly can have with nearly the entire nervous system.

The word causes the image to be reborn, thus giving life to the object. It provides a category that specifies a collective, social designation. It virtually makes the perceived object reappear on the level of sight. It possesses it to the inner most depths of the same linguistic group. In this case it is true that the word allows the projected object-images to be perceived as well as the things they evoke to march past, depending on the time it takes for the language to flow by. In the linguistic chain, different designated elements arrive as defined by the order that has been established.

On the other hand, if the object remains the sole reminder of sound that describes it and if its representation remains ideographical, then the object reminds us of the word. But it is like speaking Chinese in the literal sense of the term. If only image and vision were involved, we would be like the completely deaf Chinese person deprived of the supportive transcribed sign, or more specifically, of the object described. One should not underestimate the complications involved here. If they are not insurmountable, they can nevertheless scarcely be diminished.

Pioneers in the field of handwriting, the Chinese were also attracted to the ideogram, a very extravagant system. Man spoke in a very correct manner before writing was born. Unfortunately, linguistics has too often forgotten this reality and has studied the language in its graphic representations. These written representations followed the spoken word and necessarily came much later. In fact, writing is very recent, only a few thousand years old — two or three or perhaps four thousand years old. It is the "magnetic" tape inscribed on paper, coded in different ways, using techniques that were successful and elaborate to varying degrees and that could be pictorial, ideographic, or phonetic in form.

■ Linguistic Economy

Everything changes in this world. Unsettled in their continuation, changing in their permanence, spoken language proceeds in the same way. They are the expression of a humanity that is never the same, regardless of appearances. Do we not live in a universe where everything evolves at an astronomical speed? And then everything follows: education, machines, men and words finally must follow in order to grasp all which is constantly being revised.

Certainly there is no reason to be ecstatic like Giambattista Vico or de Marr about the evolutions or projections instilled in Humboldt's time. Without doubt, Martinet's approach is safer; he followed his predecessors — Whitney, Sapir, for example — in their references to descriptions of economy. Without exhausting the subject, he at least knew how to strip the subject down to the bare bones and make it intelligible so that from then on we could observe the inescapable shifts that a whole group of disconcerting, if foreseeable, modifications generated.

In recent years, linguistics has experienced real internal revolutions, as much a result of the considerable contributions of nineteenth century research following the discovery of Sanskrit as of the consequences that derived from it. We recall Scheigel's theories, followed by those held by Bopp, Grimm, and Humboldt. Schleicher's linguistic-botanic epic comes to mind. But it was necessary to absorb all of them, to allow for a period of quiet capable of normalizing all of the tumultuous waves that followed exposure to the works of Ferdinand de Saussure, Troubetzkoy, Jakobson, Meillet, and Martinet.

Then a calmer, less frenetic period allowed a few ideas to be gleaned, perfected, and pushed to their extremes with the aim of coming to grips with linguistics itself. We must admit that linguistics has not yet settled. A sudden ground swell, like a hurricane has upset the "whole" that had been assembled to date, calling everything in question all over again, and obliging specialists to rethink linguistics from yet another angle so as to enrich and liberate it from certain constraints. But all of this has taken time.

This new stir originated largely in the increasingly important invasion of mathematics into the midst of logistic studies. More precisely, the dimension that certain investigators attempted to introduce, as supporting an obvious rationality, in fact did nothing more than represent the formulation of the operational logic of a well-structured thought.

On the face of it, it is something like an atoll emerging from the water; this event was supported on the foundations already extensively developed by Guillaume, Hjemslev, Fant and Halle. But it is Harris we should credit with the release of the floods. At that time he was indebted to Barhillel's logico-mathematical concepts, crystallized around the novel idea of automatic translation. The launching platform for the famous bomb was thus constructed. The bomb took flight and shook the world of linguistics. Sparks flew in all directions. Many repercussions were recorded. The consequences have only just begun to be seen as the sky clears, now that the smoke is dissipating.

Without doubt, with the help of time — man's fabulous ally — an account of this period will be made possible. We will know if we have taken a step upwards on the ladder of truth or if we have to go back to the drawing board. Thanks to the theories of Chomsky, linguistics once again was caught up in sensation, wonder, and at the same time, disarray. But even ten years after its thundering entrance, not enough time has sufficed to sift through the side effects caused by this sudden invasion.

■ The Linguistic Evidence

As we have already established, the evidence in this field cannot yet be cited. And yet if the linguistic evidence is to manifest itself, it can do so only on a firm foundation of multiple certainties. For example, we can no longer deny the innate nature of speech. Only man is endowed with this faculty so that it can distinctively represent him. The fact that this innate nature evolved parallel to thought is also based on solid, undeniable foundations. Can one argue that thought could exist without language? Yes, certainly, but in order for this multi-dimensional thought to take off and optimize its creativity, speech has to be brought to it because its time dimension provides thoughts with a quasi-infinitely varied developmental structure.

It is no longer feasible to maintain the law of systematic elimination of all psychological resonances in regard to language. The interweaving is such that we can suggest, without being too far from the truth, that the one does not progress without the other. The rule that both must be present is equally to be allowed; it is necessary to take into account all of the subtlety and caution necessary to the placement of the interferences and connections that bind them.

One cannot deny that communication must really exist so that the social group can elaborate itself and grow to the level of an ethnic group. This confirmation can only be accomplished to the extent that it binds this communication to a mutual listening, just as much as it is true that to talk means to listen to the other. It means giving a person the opportunity of expressing himself, of affirming himself, of existentially inserting himself into the community. It also implies making him resonate at a high level; and this demands an art, a skill, a courtesy that allows him to maintain, to animate, and to lead the listener to share the idea by means of a thought that is both common and personal to each individual concerned.

Each demand attains full power by becoming evidence, even that of self-listening, of controlling oneself to play the body of the other in order to train him to put himself into reflexive syntony. Not that one insists on convincing one's listener, nor that one has to lead him into a particular line of thought. The aim is to bring the protagonists into lyrical harmony so as to create the communicative liaison. It is having the idea pass from one to the other in a given language in such a way that it is understood and yet still personally perceived.

And so we arrive at a new direction that is really an original field of exploration. This approach is concerned with psychology and linguistics as well as with all aspects of the other human sciences. Because neither their particular nature is threatened nor their existential tie thrown off, their functions, oneness, and universality are revealed through diverse investigations in which one measures understanding, vastness, richness, and density. Their respective autonomies are assured by the characteristics of not being "assaulted" by erosion of their limits nor invasion of their boundaries. In effect, while language recaptures its dimension and reason for being, not only are the differences discovered between languages, but also their common roots and identical foundations.

No doubt one can dive into profound reflection concerning these concepts, perhaps from a metaphysical angle or on a materialistic plane. One can catch a glimpse of the sky or even sink into the depths of the material. One can strive to imagine a way of creating models of the celestial world or the concrete environment. And why not develop simulations of animal or human physiology? Whether one is acting out of love or out of duty to some more obscure requirement of the work, the underlying dynamic remains the same.

■ The Powers of Listening

Regardless of the discipline addressed, research uncovers the same roots. Energetically speaking, life is the common factor that is translated into a manifestation capable of being perceived by the act of listening. This exceptional capacity allows us to decipher the universe in all its dimensions. Man is the biological response to this energy, which is evident in so many forms that it eludes our comprehension. Energy that moves the cosmos, solar energy, atomic energy, vital energy... It is certainly difficult to conceive that all are from the same phenomenon, but it truly is from the same thing, only it is phenomenologically expressed in diverse ways.

As for listening, it is a unique and all-embracing faculty that commands the nervous system and the sensory organs in order to decipher this multiform energy. Perception attempts to recuperate it, to circumvent it, to utilize it, even though it does not manage to completely understand it. It is simultaneously too subtle and too powerful to be actually considered from a holistic aspect.

But all of that does not at all prevent our being able to make use of it. Was water not used long before its composition was known? And who can explain its physical-chemical structure even now? Nor can the mystery of electricity, a significant part of our lives, be satisfactorily explained.

Listening is, in a way, the most elaborate manifestation of the ensemble of our perceptions working in a synergistic manner under the control of the ear. We now know, after all that we have said about it, that the ear is not only man's most essential organ but is also his "neurological body." Engaged in listening, the nervous system thus becomes a springboard for the listener. But unfortunately, humanity only imperfectly and incompletely uses this fabulous mirror, which reflects the material world and the heavens, which captures ideas and diffuses them, which perceives reality and passes by illusion. It does this so well that one could say that the brain is the annex of the "listening man" and that the more he listens, the more human he becomes.

Thus we see at what level the linguistic dimension is embedded. It does not make language an instrument. It makes a verbal secretion of it, the result of multiple integrations effected by addressing another and controlling oneself. Everything has a significant value as soon as it transmits emotional, intentional, or semantic information.

The rhythms and intonations depend on the sonority of the materials offered, on the available acoustics. It is well known that we cannot use a metal object in the same way as a wooden object. The differences are as sensitive and varied as with ethnic rhythm and intonations. The interaction of the semantemes already appears in a child's babble; at that point one single word represents in essence the whole language. If a child but delivers his first "papas" in French, or in Italian, or in Spanish or if only a "dad" is emitted in English, the social language emerges, with its inflections, dynamics, and flow.

Other language is that which is transplanted on a deficient body instrument, because the body itself is the instrument of language. When this happens, the general organization of communication is distorted and will "misrepresent" all that is expressed. All will be marred by distortions. The rash of learning problems definitely find their origin here. We know today that these problems can for the most part be corrected by educating the ear and by reorganizing the audiolinguistic circuits.

This overshadowing of the body as instrument of verbalization introduces a world without language similar to that of the schizophrenic. Thanks to the technological advances that have been made, it is now possible to reawaken the desire to listen, that is to say, the desire to get in tune with the ear-brain-man listening structure.

If we emphasize instrumental dimensions, it is because numerous distortions can intervene, render socialization difficult and complicated, and sometimes create rejection. Indeed, if the instrument (i.e., the body) is not imbued with a desire to listen, if areas of the body are ignored, forgotten, eliminated, or lost through scotoma, they will then only evolve for their own account, isolated from the whole body until organic deviations or discriminations are created. Psychosomatic illnesses originate where this lack of dialogue with the body occurs, in the absence of listening. Besides, if the instrument is abnormal due to organic deficiencies in the initial structure, as a result of birth defects or accident, it will help us if we can re-establish listening that is specially adapted to this new apparatus. It will be necessary to change the vestibulo-cochlear system. If finally the intelligence potential is weak, it will become necessary to provide it with a lot of stimuli so that its lesser potentialities may be exploited to the maximum. It is through listening, which constitutes in fact the generator motor that energizes the nervous system, that such a result can be obtained.

■ Conclusion

The role attributed to the ear was already very large in 1963 when this book was first published. This importance has been strongly affected and amplified by us since then, due to the very specific research that we have carried out in this field. After more than twenty-five years in this and associated fields, we find that the ear largely exceeds what we thought it could do when we set out to write this book. Language tied to this concept of self-control has allowed consolidation, fortification, and self-imposition of the evidence that the ear is actually the fundamental feature that makes man what he is: vertical, speaker, creator, socially aware, and communicator.

It is through listening that man rediscovers the reason for his existence: communion with his neighbor, with creation, and with his creator. But this is so far over his head that all that man attributes to it constitutes a reduction, which is sometimes unacceptable and certainly always incomprehensible. And yet in the innermost depths of each human being, in his unfathomable heart, is ontologically reflected this Logos that brings with it the breath of inspiration and energy. It is there, living, so that the desire to be will develop, the desire to live and the desire to love in spite of existential barriers and problems.

Humanity is advancing toward a dimension of listening that is growing and moving toward complete comprehension, resulting from the growth of a more evenly distributed consciousness. This is the dimension of common sense that is discovering the evidence.

In the future, this transcendent listening ability, which has been accorded to the universe in so far as it is possible to achieve it in reality, will rescue man from the meanderings of his cluttered psyche so that he can discover the light that lives within him beyond the darkness that clouds his mind.

At the time of the first edition, we thought that this book could only end with an "au revoir." No doubt this addition will provoke other encounters; thanks to the advances of an ever more sophisticated technology, the discoveries of today are witnessing an exponential acceleration. It goes without saying that we support these new projects all the more strongly since they are confirming our investigations, enriching our approach to the subject, and giving us further food for thought.

■ Bibliography

Ajuriaguerra, J. de and Hecaen H. *Le Cortex cérébral.* Paris: Mason, 1960.

Baecker, L. de *Grammaire comparée des langues de la France.* Paris: Ch. Blériot, 1860.

Békésy, G. von, *Experiments in Hearing,* McGraw-Hill, 1963.

Bergson, H. *L'Evolution créatrice.* Paris: PUF, 1957.

Bréal, M., *Les Commencements du Verbe, (Revue de Paris),* 15, 12, 1899.

Chomsky, N., *Transformational Analysis,* doctoral thesis, 1995; *The Logical Basis in Linguistic Theory,* microfilm, 1956; *Syntactic Structure,* La Haye, Mouton, 1957; *Current Issues in Linguistic Theory,* La Haye, Mouton, 1964; *Topic in the theory of generative grammar,* La Haye, Mouton, 1966;

Dauzat, G. *Le Génie de la langue française,* Paris, Payot, 1953.

Février, J. *Histoire de l'écriture,* Paris, Payot, 1959.

Garcia, A. *Les Troubles du langage.* Paris, Masson, 1951.

Grammont, M. *Traité de phonétique.* Paris, Delagrave, 1960.

Harris, Z. S., *Structural Linguistic,* Chicago, University of Chicago Press, 1960.

Head, H. *Aphasia and Kindred Disorders of Speech,* New York, MacMillan, 1926.

Hecaen, H. and Ajuriaguerra, J de. *Méconnaissances et halluci-nations corporelles.* Paris, Masson, 1952.

Hyelmslev, L. *Prolégomènes, Paris,* Éd de Minuit, 1968.

Jakobson, R. *Phonological Studies,* La Haye, Mouton, 1962

Jespersen, O. *Progress in Language.* Londres, Swam & Sonneshein, 1894.

Jousse, M. *Les Récitatifs rythmiques parallèles.* Paris, Spes, 1929.

Leibnitz, G.W.V. *Nouveaux essais sur l'entendement humain,* nouvelle édition, Flammarion, 1990.

Martinet, A. *Économie des changements phonétiques*, Berne, Éd. A. Francke, 1955.

Marty, A. *Gesammelte Schriften*. 1916.

Marty, A. *Über den Ursprung der Sprache*. 1975.

Marty, A. *Untersuchungen zur Grundlegung der Allegemeinen Grammatik und Sprachphilosophie*. Halle, 1908.

Meillet, A. *Introduction à l'étude comparative des langues indoeuropéennes*. Paris, Hachette, 1922.

Ombredane, A. *L'Aphasie et l'elaboration de la pensée explicite*. Paris, Hachette, 1951.

Pei, M. *Histoire du langage*. Paris, Payot, 1954.

Piaget, J. *Le Langage et la pensée*. Neuchâtel, Delachaux & Niestlé, 1923.

Renan, E. *De l'origine du langage*. Paris, Didier, 1987.

Revesz, G. *Origine et préhistoire du langage*. Paris, Payot, 1950.

Sapir E. *Langage*. Paris, Payot, 1970.

Saussure, F de. *Cours de linguistique générale*. Paris, Payot, 1989.

Troubetzkoy, N.S. *Grundzuege der Phonologie*. Paris, Klincksieck, 1967.

Vico, J.B. *Sciencia Nueva*, 1725.

Whitney, W.D. *La Vie du langage*. Paris, Germer-Baillière, 1875.

Wundt, W. *Die Sprache*. Leipzig, 1912.

Wundt, W. *Elementen der Völkerpsychologie*. Leipzig, 1912.

Wundt, W. *Logik*. 1922.

Wundt, W. *Sprachgeschichte und Sprachpsychologie*. Leipzig, 1901.

◼ AFTERWORD

◼ DESCRIPTION OF THE TOMATIS METHOD & LISTENING TEST

Billie M. Thompson, Ph.D.

I have worked with the Tomatis Method for nearly a decade as a certified Consultant. Much of my time is spent describing what the Method is, how it works, and in what ways we evaluate the ear's performance when we give a Tomatis Listening Test, whose protocol is different from a hearing test. This Afterword tells exactly how the Method works and what is included in the assessment that determines the basis for developing a program for a person.

I have been privileged to edit in English this book and Tomatis's autobiography, *The Conscious Ear*. I hope that both books will allow others to learn about this dynamic method that has provided assistance to countless people of all ages and their families.

I invite people also to look at a chapter titled "Dr. Mozart" in Paul Chukow's biography *Depardieu* (Alfred Knopf, Inc. 1994), in which the outstanding French actor of his generation acknowledges Tomatis for his significant role in helping Gerard achieve his potential. Certainly the success story of someone like Depardieu, whose language ability is clearly superior in his profession, belongs somewhere in the accolades for the Tomatis Method and the discussion of the ear's role in language development and use.

One could generally describe the Tomatis Method as a sound stimulation and educational intervention that improves listening, language, motivation, attention, learning, self image, awareness, musical ability and appreciation, audio-vocal control, and posture.

It begins with an Initial Assessment, which includes tests of listening and laterality and some drawings. A consultation follows to review the results of the assessment and the detailed personal history to determine appropriate goals for the person, and to recommend a program if one can be helpful in achieving the goals.

The human ear has the functional capabilities to do at least the following:

1. Perceive sound,
2. Process sound without distortion,
3. Discriminate between higher and lower frequencies of sound,
4. Perceive spatial origin of sounds,
5. Attend to sounds we want to hear and tune out ones we don't want,
6. Stimulate the brain with sensory input,
7. Integrate sensory information from muscle movement,
8. Establish good balance/equilibrium,
9. Control phonation,
10. Control musical ability.

These functions can be altered at any age by accident, illness, or emotional or physical trauma. By using the Method developed by Dr. Tomatis, it is possible to restore to the ears their essential effectiveness when the cause is not conductive or sensorineural damage. It should be noted that sometimes what appears to be solely an organic or sensorineural difficulty can be at least partly due to poor functioning, delayed development, or tuning out undesirable information. When poor functioning occurs, poor self-esteem and low motivation may follow.

A well-functioning ear is described as a good listening ear. It can tune in across the entire sound spectrum to sounds it wants to hear and tune out those it does not want. It can perceive and analyze every part of the frequency spectrum with maximum speed and precision. It integrates muscle movement received from the entire body. A good ear is mirrored by a voice with good tone and quality. That is, a good voice reflects a good ear. We listen, speak, sing, read, write, and learn with our ears.

The Listening Test identifies listening strengths and weaknesses. Generally, the ideal listening ear has these capabilities:

1. Hearing *threshold* within normal range.
2. An open auditory *selectivity* to identify and compare higher and lower frequencies of sounds.
3. A precise auditory *spatialization* to identify the source of direction of the sound.
4. An ascending curve *slope* up to 3000-4000 Hz with stabilization at this level and a slight drop in the highest frequencies, to allow easier discrimination between sounds.
5. An *attention* to externally perceived sounds we want to hear and the ability to tune out those we do not want, and the *parallel perception* of bone and air conducted sounds over the frequency spectrum.
6. *Evenness* of reception and an absence of distortion and stress in the response curve of the ear.
7. *Balance* of bone and air reception within and between both ears.
8. A *right audio-vocal lead ear* as the most efficient pathway directly to the speech center in the left brain hemisphere.
9. Vestibular integration of muscle and sensory information for effective *motor coordination*.
10. Reception of high frequency sounds to *stimulate* the brain.

The failure of one or several of these parameters provokes a disharmony that results in impaired listening and, consequently, deficient learning and self-esteem. Others who know a person (such as parents, teachers, and employers) can observe symptoms of poor listening in areas of receptive language, expressive language, sensory motor integration, and behavior/attitude.

In order to assist the human ear to establish or re-establish its full potential, Dr. Tomatis developed a method now used in many countries around the world. Listening sessions and interim tests and consultations are scheduled following the Initial Assessment. Usually it is better to begin with an intensive training, but a more extended initial program over a longer period can be used in some instances. Each listening program has three phases: auditory (receptive) training, breaks for integration, and audio-vocal (expressive) training. The first phase is primarily passive in developing a better listening. The second phase allows the person time to experience, integrate, and habituate the new listening patterns. In the third phase, the person continues at a prescribed rate over several more weeks to develop the audio-vocal control necessary to maintain the gains. This occurs with sufficient active session practice with one's own voice heard with a good quality and may require several eight-day audio-vocal intensives. This goes back to the premise cited in this book, that the voice can only produce what the ear can hear.

The length of program varies depending on the person's motivation and degree of difficulty. With many people who are very cut off from others or who have suffered central nervous system damage, the program may extend over a year or longer with many breaks for integration. A typical length of program is sixty hours of listening sessions spread over several months, with the actual length determined at reassessment. One typically starts with a fifteen-day intensive, followed by a break of three or four weeks, then an eight-day intensive, followed by another break of four to six weeks, and another eight-day intensive.

During the training the person listens to sounds of music and voice that have been filtered to stimulate the improved focusing ability of the ear. By increasing the selective power of the ear, the person can perceive sound with less distortion and analyze it more precisely over the whole frequency range, from fundamental frequencies to the highest harmonics.

For a non-trained ear, the fundamental frequency of a sound too often masks its harmonic spectrum, and the person has difficulty in controlling voice timbre (the mix of higher harmonics). Consequently, the voice stays flat, with no modulation. By improving listening, the speaker has the opportunity to improve voice quality, fluency, modulation, and articulation, for the benefit of him- or herself (as one's own first listener) and others who listen. Implications for education and the workplace are vast. When one's voice conveys energy and interest to others, the invitation to listen is more readily accepted.

The program can help the musician who is unable to adjust his or her ear to listen to the harmonics of the sounds emitted by voice or instrument to better regulate the melody.

Besides the ear, the whole body listens. Good listeners become aware of and acquire a correct listening posture during the auditory-vocal training phase of the program. They develop an erect but not stiff spine, a slight forward tilt of the head with eyes closed, a relaxed neck and jaw, and open chest to allow ample breathing. The posture is easiest when sitting on a high stool or standing with the small of the back against a wall and when listening to the high frequency sounds of the filtered music.

Audio-vocal sessions consist of repetition of words and phrases alternated with sessions of singing and music (filtered or non-filtered). The words and phrases progressively train the ear to listen for the entire harmonic range of sound information. Because the larynx emits only those harmonics that the ear hears (proven at the Sorbonne in 1957 and known as the Tomatis Effect), the word, sentence, or musical phrase is emitted with greater control. When the ear listens well, the whole body is involved. Learning becomes easier, and more potential skill and intelligence can be developed.

As a follow-up to the audio-vocal program, the person is strongly advised to practice some phonatory exercises every day for a minimum of half an hour. He or she is given an exercise of reading aloud while maintaining good audio-vocal posture and holding the right hand close to the right of the mouth to strengthen right audio-vocal dominance, so that the voice quality, rhythm, and flow will improve.

Once the person has completed just the passive phase of the program, he or she is more motivated and better able to work with teachers and other professionals, such as psychologists and psychiatrists, speech language pathologists, physical and occupational therapists, osteopaths and physicians whose specialties involve using language, posture, motivation, and motor control. The person is better able to learn in the formal traditional educational settings and to more easily develop skills that once were very difficult.

While many researchers are just beginning to investigate and report on the impact of the ear in our lives, this book shows that Tomatis developed not just a theory but also a practical method of approaching the source of many dysfunctional problems. It is a Method that is surprisingly quick and has many long-range impacts on a person's learning, communication, attitude and well-being. It is time for the Tomatis Method to expand throughout the English-speaking world. *The Ear and Language* will help in this effort.

Billie M. Thompson, Ph.D.
Phoenix, 1996

■ Index

■ ILLUSTRATIONS

pp. 2, 3, Church of Saint-Marie-Madeleine, Aix-en-Provence: *le Maître de l'Annonciation* (detail); p.4, bas relief from the Saint Wandrille Abbey (detail); pp. 52-53, Henriques: *Le Repas de la Sainte Famille*; p. 57, drawing of Léonard de Vinci; pp. 61 and 126/127, Michealangelo: a drawing and *Creation of Adam*; p. 64, Berthe Morisot: *The Cradle*; pp. 68-69, J. Bosch: *le concert dans l'oeuf* (detail); p. 70, Valentin: *The Concert* (detail); pp. 94 and 108/109, Jérôme Bosch; p. 98, Van Gogh: *Self Portrait*; p. 116, Dürer: *Head of a Child*; pp. 156/157, Caravage: *Narcissus*; p. 158, Rodin: *The Thinker*.

Catherine Du Vivier: pp. 140/141; Chavignier: p. 22; Dr. Tomatis: pp. 80a, 81b, 88, 114, 150/151, 152/153, 160/161, 171, 172, 173, 176; Singer Metrics Division: p. 86; Staatliche Museen zu Berlin: pp. 10/11; Giraudon: pp. 2/3, 30/31, 61, 64, 68/69, 94, 108/109, 110, 126/127, 142, 156/157; Bulloz: pp. 70, 98; Roland Bardet/Édit. du Seuil: 4, 90, 92/93, 103, 124/125, 158; Archives Éd. du Seuil: p. 133; National Library/Éd. du Seuil: pp. 8, 14, 16, 26, 32, 36, 40, 41, 43, 44/45, 48, 54, 57, 128, 166; Schémas/Éd. du Seuil: pp. 25, 49, 73, 74, 80b, 81a, 84, 99; Travaux photographiques: Publicité R. Bardet.

■ TOMATIS CENTERS

INFORMATION ABOUT CENTERS WORLDWIDE

FRANCE   Tomatis International, S.A.
6, place de la Republique Dominicaine
75017 Paris
331-42-12-83-70   FAX 331-42-12-83-79
Christian Tomatis

UNITED STATES

ARIZONA   Sound Listening & Learning Center (Tomatis Center)
Phoenix   2701 E. Camelback Rd., Suite 205
Phoenix, AZ 85016
(602) 381-0086   FAX (602) 957-6741
Director: Billie M. Thompson, Ph.D.

CALIFORNIA   Tomatis Listening and Learning Center
Lafayette   3700 Mount Diable Blvd., Suite 300
Lafayette, CA 94549
(510) 284-8431   FAX (510) 283-0961
Director: Pierre Sollier, M.F.C.C.

CALIFORNIA   Sound Listening & Learning Center (Tomatis Center)
Pasadena   200 E. Del Mar, Suite 208
Pasadena, CA 91105
(818) 405-2386   FAX (818) 405-2387
Director: Billie M. Thompson, Ph.D.

COLORADO   Center for InnerChange
Denver   55 Madison Street, Suite 375
Denver, CO 80206
(303) 320-4411   FAX (303) 322-5550
Director: Ron Minson, M.D.

LOUISIANA   Institute for Human Potential
Metairie   The Listening Centre
3901 Houma Blvd., Suite 109
Metairie, LA 70006
(504) 887-6270   FAX (504) 454 6337
Directors: Suzie Andrews, Ph.D., Michelle Trumps, OTR

MARYLAND The Spectrum Center
Bethesda   4715 Cordell Avenue, 3rd Floor West
            Bethesda, MD 20814
            (301) 657-0988 FAX (301) 657-0989
            Directors: Valerie DeJean, OTR, Patricia Dixon, Ph.D.

MASSACHUSETTS   The Listening Center-Amherst
Amherst   135 Summer Street, Amherst, MA 01002
            (413) 549-0901 FAX (413) 253-7901
            Director: Elizabeth Verrill, M.A.

OREGON   Center for Communication & Learning Skills
Lake Oswego 14674 Rainbow Drive, Lake Oswego, OR 97035
             (503) 699-9022 FAX (503) 636-3014
             Director: Judy Belk, Ph.D.

TEXAS   The Listening Centre
Dallas   12800 Hillcrest, Suite 101, Dallas, TX 75230
            (214) 404-8152 FAX (214) 392-0532
            Directors: Ursula Palmer, Ph.D.,
            Harl & Jim Asaff, Emilia Flores

CANADA

ONTARIO   The Listening Centre
Toronto   599 Markham Street
            Toronto, Ontario M6G 2L7
            (416) 588-4136 FAX (416) 588-4459
            Director: Paul Madaule

SASKATCHEWAN   C.A.L.L.
Regina   208 – 408 Broad Street
            Regina, Saskatchewan S4R 1X3
            (306) 543-9951 FAX (306) 584-1187
            Director: Bob Roy, Ph.D.

TOMATIS CENTERS – MEXICO & CENTRAL AMERICA

COSTA RICA   Institute de Tomatis Costa Rica
San Jose   Apartado Postal 888-1011
            San Jose, Costa Rico
            (506) 227-4413 FAX (506) 226-8503
            Director: Arturo Gatgens, M.D.

MEXICO Guadalajara	Estimulacion Auditiva de Guadalajara Terranova 1440, Col. Providencia, C.P. 44620 Guadalajara, Jalisco 52-36-42-46-51 FAX 52-36-41-45-58 Director: Gloria G. de Assmar, Claudia Gonzales
MEXICO Mexico City	Centro De Estimulacion Auditiva Sierra Mojada 329, Col. Lomas de Chapultepec 11000 Mexico, D.F. 52-55-40-20-93 FAX 52-55-20-09-47 Directors: Georgina A. de Moreno, M.A. Virginia Chenillo, M.A., Gloria G. de Assmar
MEXICO Mexico City	Centro Tomatis San Jose Cordobanes #23, San Jose Insurgentes 039000 Mexico, D.F. 52-56-80-02-76 FAX 52-593-1251 Director: Georgina A. de Moreno, M.A.
MEXICO Mexico City	Centro de Estimulacion Auditiva Sur, S.C. Chimalcoyotl #169 Colonia Toriello Guerra Tlalpan, D.F. 52-56-06-81-79 FAX 52-56-06-26-99 Director: Virginia Chenillo, M.A.
MEXICO Monterrey	Centro Escucha Monterrey Vasconcelos #1561, Pte. Int. 2, Col. Del Valle Garza Garcia, N.L. 66240 52-83-36-61-36 FAX 52-83-99-56-56 Directors: Eva S. de Jimenez, Rufigio R. de Menchaca
MEXICO Torreon	Centro Escucha Torreon Guadalquivir #406, Colonia Navarro Torreon, Coahuila 52-17-13-52-94 Director: Dra. Christina Jimenez de Reza
PANAMA Panama City	Centro Auditivo Tomatis Panama Avenida Cuba #54, Appartado 55-2593, Estefeta Paitilla Panama City, Republic of Panama (507) 263-2731 Director: Eve Wiznitzer

ABOUT THE EDITOR

Billie M. Thompson, Ph.D., is the Director of Sound Listening & Learning Centers in Phoenix, Arizona and Pasadena, California. She also edited the English translation of Tomatis' autobiography, *The Conscious Ear.*